TEACHING READING SKILLS IN CONTENT AREAS:

a practical guide to the construction of student exercises

Second Edition

GAIL B. WEST

FLORIDA TECHNOLOGICAL UNIVERSITY

Sandpiper Press, Inc.
P. O. Box 1059
Oviedo, Florida 32765

Library of Congress Catalog Card Number: 78-53125

International Standard Book Number: 0-914666-01-0

Printed in the United States of America

10 9 8 7 6 5 4 3 2 1

TABLE OF CONTENTS

PREFACE

The revision of this workbook has been put off for a couple of years; but, for once, procrastination has been to good purpose. In checking the bibliographies upon the completion of a first draft in January, 1978, it was found that several new titles and second editions were scheduled for spring publication. Reading in the content areas continues to be an area of growing interest and concern as evidenced by the fact that no fewer than twelve new titles and revisions have appeared since late 1977.

Since it is intended that this workbook be keyed to the major textbooks in the field, it was necessary to wait through the spring in order to be able to prepare the Keys which are to be found inside the front and back covers as well as at the end of each chapter.

In preparing this second edition, all of the chapters have been completely revised and expanded. Some new topics have been added. More sample exercises have been included. Nevertheless, it is hoped that the relative simplicity and practicality of the first edition have been retained.

HOW TO USE THIS WORKBOOK

The purpose of this workbook is to help you, the content area teacher, identify the skills and processes students need to perform well within your discipline; to evaluate their abilities to use these skills and processes; and to develop your competence in constructing reading exercises to improve these skills, based on the content materials used in your classroom.

1

The chapters include a rationale for the activities, background information, definitions of key terms, and sample exercises. At the end of each chapter is a KEY TO TEXTBOOKS in which sections of the textbooks listed inside the front cover have been keyed to the chapter topic. The books are listed by authors' names. Since it is keyed to major texts, this workbook can be used as a supplement to the text you might be using in a course, component, or workshop. Or, it can be used alone with referral to the listed selections.

Keep in mind that this is a workbook. It is not intended to be a definitive textbook. There are blank pages in the book because the most important parts will be written by you. Rather than merely reading about reading, you will have opportunities to apply what you have read. Exercises have been proposed after each chapter, 2 through 10.

One way to carry out the activities in this workbook is to select a textbook in the area of interest to you and to base all of your exercises on that particular text, using supplementary materials when appropriate. In this way, the exercises you prepare can be used immediately in your classroom. If you are not presently teaching, the experience of working closely with one book should enable you to design similar kinds of exercises for any reading materials you might use.

THE IMPORTANCE OF ASKING GOOD QUESTIONS

Since questioning is the quintessential aspect of teaching, most of the exercises in this workbook are question-asking in nature. Good teachers, whatever other excellent qualities they may have, also ask good questions. They teach students to ask good questions, perhaps more through the example they provide in the course of their own excellent teaching, than by the direct instruction they offer. They provoke critical thinking through the asking of questions which require students to discover facts, compare and contrast, notice cause and effect, clarify relationships, analyze, synthesize, identify assumptions and opinions, evaluate, draw conclusions, find alternatives, solve problems, illustrate with examples, etc.

Questioning is so important to education that modules, articles, books, models, audio-tapes and videocassettes on the subject have been produced in abundance. In *Teaching As a Subversive Activity,* Postman and Weingartner write:

> The art and science of asking questions is the source of all knowledge. Any curriculum of a new education would, therefore, have to be centered around question asking ... Question asking and answer finding go hand in hand. And answer finding requires that students go to books, to laboratories to newspapers, to TV sets, to the streets, to wherever they must go to find the answers.[1]

---

[1]Neil Postman and Charles Weingartner, *Teaching As A Subversive Activity,* (New York: Delacorte Press, 1969), p. 89.

Appendix A of this workbook, entitled "Some Elements of the Art of Questioning," has been drawn largely from a long and useful chapter in *A Handbook for the Teaching of Social Studies* by The Association of Teachers of Social Studies in the City of New York.[2] The information contained in this Appendix may be helpful not only in preparing written questions, but also in the preparation of lesson plans and in leading class discussions.

An important point to be emphasized in regard to questioning is this: *testing is not teaching.* In a class discussion, the purpose is generally to teach. In writing exercises to develop and extend reading skills, the purpose is also to teach. This is the sort of questioning which you will be asked to do as you prepare the exercises suggested by this workbook. The purpose is not to see what students already know for the purpose of assigning grades, but to lead them to organize what they know and build upon this knowledge to gain further insight and develop new concepts.

[2]Association of Teachers of Social Studies in the City of New York, *A Handbook for the Teaching of Social Studies,* (Boston: Allyn and Bacon, Inc.,), 1977.

ACKNOWLEDGEMENTS

Authors always acknowledge that many people have contributed to the production of their books. They do it because it is true. Most books would never be written nor published if one had to do it alone. This book is no exception. There are many who could be named here, but specifically I would like to thank the many students who have contributed exercises which are used as examples throughout. Also, a great deal of appreciation is expressed to Carol McCrea whose careful editing, creative suggestions, and constant encouragement shaped the book to its final form.

GAIL B. WEST

1

READING AND THE CONTENT AREA TEACHER

THE READING SITUATION

Many teachers are confronted daily with large numbers of students who simply cannot "do" English or social studies or mathematics. Students often cannot do the work because they lack the reading-study-thinking skills that would enable them to make sense out of the material.

Research bears this out. In many of the nation's schools, over half of the students are reading two years or more below grade level which classifies them as "retarded readers." Moreover, many of our high school graduates are functionally illiterate, that is, they lack skills and knowledge needed for meeting the ordinary requirements of adult living. A recent study (1975) headed by Norvell Northcutt of the University of Texas suggested that 51 percent of the 18-29 age group did not have what former U.S. Commissioner of Education, Terrel H. Bell, termed "cope-ability." Data from this study also indicated that 20 percent of the American population (over 23 million) did not know the meaning of an industry sign which read, "We Are An Equal Opportunity Employer." Some 15 million were unable to address an envelope well enough to assure that the Postal Service could deliver it. Bell noted that these millions cannot really cope, "not because they cannot read, but because they cannot understand what they read. Either they don't pay enough attention to what words mean or they simply have not had sufficient basic education."[1]

Many of these functionally illiterate persons go to college. The student newspaper at the University of Florida reported in 1975 that approximately one out

---

[1] George Neill, "Washington Report," *Phi Delta Kappan,* (Jan., 1976), p. 355.

5

of every 20 students enrolled at the U of F was functionally illiterate. Dr. A. Garr Cranney, head of the U of F Reading and Study Skills Center, conducted the test. He noted that these students were in a "special admit" category, but they were still considered qualified students.[2] This problem is not limited to the University of Florida. Many of the major textbook publishers are rewriting some college textbooks down to the ninth-grade reading level because so many students entering college are poor readers.

If that isn't startling enough, some of these students graduate from college and become teachers! In another recent study (1976), it was revealed that some prospective teachers couldn't read as well as the top eighth-graders![3] Obviously, there is a reading problem in this country.

Compounding the problem is the fact that in the nation's public schools, there are not enough reading specialists to work with all of the students who need assistance, nor are regular classroom teachers prepared to help. Furthermore, there are some popular misconceptions about "reading" that cause some content teachers to shrink from approaching the problem.

THE READING PROCESS

Some teachers who have not been trained in reading may have the notion that reading instruction is a mysterious activity conducted in a laboratory amongst strange machinery and multi-colored, multi-leveled, esoterically coded materials—strictly the province of the specialist. To the untrained, the environment in which *remedial reading* takes place, where the main objective is to teach the most basic skills of reading, might indeed look unfamiliar. However, learning to read and learning to read content are not synonymous. The reading teacher's job is to teach the skills that are fundamental to all reading, while the content area teacher's role in reading is to guide students in the application of these skills and strategies to classroom materials. Content teachers, therefore, need not be reading specialists, but they must be consciously aware of the skills and thinking processes needed to "make sense" of reading materials.

Reading is a process—a thinking process—which must be directly taught and reinforced through guided practice. Arthur Gates described the process in this way:

> Reading is not a simple mechanical skill; nor is it a narrow scholastic tool. Properly cultivated, it is essentially a thought process. However, to say reading is a "thought-

---

[2]Bob Beck, "High Functional Illiteracy reported at UF," *Independent Florida Alligator,* (October 3, 1975), p. 1.

[3]"Prospective Teachers' Reading Worse Than Pupils?", *Orlando Sentinel Star,* (June 4, 1976), p. 36.

getting" process is to give it too restricted a definition. It should be developed as a complex organization of patterns of higher mental processes. It can and should embrace all types of thinking—evaluating, judging, imagining, reasoning, and problem-solving. Indeed, it is believed that reading is one of the best media for cultivating many techniques of thinking and imagining.[4]

Another way of saying this, though simplistically, is that reading-learning-thinking is a continual process of relating the unfamiliar to what is already known, that is "making sense of the world."[5]

Reading is a continual process; it is also a complex one. In order to describe this complex process and render it more manageable, William S. Gray developed a model of reading in which he classified the process into four broad areas: word perception, comprehension, reaction, and integration. Though separated, Gray stresses that one must keep in mind that these aspects of reading are interrelated and form a unit. Though the model seems simple, it took Gray over thirty years to develop it.[6]

Word perception, in Gray's model, is the ability to physically see the word or symbol, then to relate it to a real object or to experience. Obviously, physiological factors, such as eyesight, hearing, and even brain damage, are involved. Some reading specialists are concerned exclusively with this aspect of reading. They use sophisticated machinery which permits observation of faulty eye movements, balanced vision, binocular vision, and so forth.

Closely related to physiological factors is book format: size of print, style of type, spacing between lines, color, and other such matters. In a broader sense, even the classroom environment has its effects: lighting, type of seating, time of day, temperature, length of time spent on instruction, distracting sights and sounds, etc.

Even if all of these factors could be controlled, the most important element in word perception—experience—would still remain uncontrollable. Experience varies, both in and out of school. Yet it is the experience of the reader that determines how well a word or picture symbol can be related to a mental image. If the reader has had no experience, taken in its broadest sense, with an "awl," when the word appears in print it will have no meaning, for the word symbol is unconnected to an image or an object. The reader may be able to identify and

---

[4]Arthur I. Gates, "Character and Purposes of the Yearbook," *Reading in the Elementary School,* Forty-eighth Yearbook of the National Society for the Study of Education, Part II. (Chicago: University of Chicago Press, 1949.) p. 3.

[5]This is Frank Smith's definition. See his *Comprehension and Learning: A Conceptual Framework for Teachers,* (New York: Holt, Rinehart, and Winston, 1975), for a detailed account of what this phrase means.

[6]W. S. Gray, "The Major Aspects of Reading," in *Sequential Development of Reading Abilities,* "Supplementary Educational Monographs," No. 90, compiled and edited by Helen M. Robinson (Chicago: University of Chicago Press, 1960), pp. 8-24.

pronounce the word, yet be unable to comprehend the meaning, the reality.

Words may be analyzed in terms of phonetic and graphic structure (prefixes, suffixes, roots); or, a dictionary may be used to elicit meaning. Even so, an unknown word in isolation is likely to mean very little. A great many words have multiple meanings; thus, to determine which meaning is intended, one must rely on context. Think of the words *bank,* and *chair,* and *run.* In isolation, the reader cannot even tell whether they are nouns or verbs. Hence, presented with a word written on a flash card, the student may be able to pronounce it without being able to tell its meaning. It is obvious that word perception without comprehension cannot legitimately be called reading, at least not in the sense that content teachers understand reading.

Comprehension is the ability to perceive relationships among a series of words, sentences or paragraphs. It goes beyond basic perception, as described above, and places meaning squarely at the center of the process.

"I deposited my money in the *bank.*" "I sat on the *bank* of a river." "I *banked* the airplane." These examples show how context illuminates meaning and enables the reader to select among several meanings of *bank.* But comprehension doesn't stop at that. Identifying the *literal* meaning of a sentence or a passage is one thing; interpreting the message, figuring out *what the author meant,* is often another. Consider the meaning of this sentence: "When Jill arrived, she was loaded for bear." As George Miller has pointed out, "The meaning of an utterance is not a linear sum of the meanings of the words that comprise it . . . In Gestalt terminology, the whole is greater than (at least, different from) the sum of its parts."[7]

At the literal level of comprehension, one distinguishes main ideas, perceives relevant details, discerns sequence, follows directions, notes conclusions. At the interpretive level of comprehension, one determines the author's purpose, notices causes and effects which may not have been directly stated, makes inferences, draws conclusions, and so forth. In other words, the reader fills in the gaps left vacant by the author, but care must be taken that these are ideas the *author* has implied, not ones which have been conjured up by the reader.

Comprehension may become difficult to *sustain* as sentence structures grow longer, more complicated in syntax, and more heavily qualified.

Reaction builds on the previous two phases. Once the reader has perceived the words in a message and linked them together to come up with a meaning, some action may result—the reader may be moved to *do* something. Reaction may be intellectual or emotional. In a class situation, students may be asked to compare an idea gained from reading with their own ideas or with those they have read

---

[7]George A. Miller, "Some Preliminaries to Psycholinguistics," in *Psycholinguistics and Reading,* edited by Frank Smith, (New York: Holt, Rinehart and Winston, 1973), p. 16.

elsewhere. Or, they may be asked to evaluate the idea, to synthesize it with other ideas, or to relate it to some experience. The ability to react in this fashion must be cultivated or taught. This is critical reading and critical thinking. It should be noted, however, that a legitimate reaction can be made only after full comprehension has been achieved.

Integration, or assimilation, is the aspect of the reading process in which readers incorporate information and/or values found through reading into their own living. Reading can change a person's outlook, philosophy, appreciations, values, even personality. This highest level of reading is the ultimate goal of education, yet it is not to be expected that every student will reach it. Teachers may do much to enable their students to reach the point at which they can integrate what they read into their living, and whether this level is attained or not will remain largely each student's own secret. This is not an aspect of reading that lends itself to measurement.

Rate of reading is a fifth aspect of reading which Helen Robinson added to Gray's model. The rate at which one reads should be related to the purpose of the reading and to the difficulty of the material. If a reader is not familiar with the vocabulary, or if the material is highly technical, the tendency is to progress more slowly than when reading light fiction. If the purpose is to evaluate ideas presented in an essay and to compare them with those expressed by another writer, reading progresses more slowly than when trying merely to get the gist of the essay. Thus, reading rate is closely associated with, even determined by, the other four aspects of the reading model.

ROLE OF THE CONTENT AREA TEACHER

Realizing, as they do, that reading is a continuous and complex process, content area teachers often misconceive their role in teaching these skills. Some have thought they would have only four days a week to teach history, for instance, if one day must be spent on reading. They have said they do not have time to cover the necessary content and teach reading/thinking in addition. This is a misconception of the way reading should be taught in the content areas. What is intended is that *while* history is being taught, the teaching of the skills and strategies necessary to understand, study, criticize, and evaluate history are incorporated—consciously incorporated. Learning theorists have long stressed that information and skills are more effectively taught within a context where they may be directly applied. It follows that reading competence improves when students focus on content and not merely on "reading." As students engage in the development of subject-matter skills, they will be learning not only the content, but

9

also *how to learn* science, or math, or geography. An example here might help illustrate that students learn content better when they are taught how to read it.

In 1966, Call and Wiggin conducted an experiment to determine if instruction in reading would contribute to the development of skills in solving word problems in mathematics. Dr. Call is a trained teacher of mathematics. Mr. Wiggin is a teacher of English with some specialization in reading who had not previously studied second-year algebra.

The experiment was conducted with two second-year algebra classes. Students in these classes were among the better students, so that it could be assumed there would be less likelihood of wide-spread deficiency in mathematics as might be found in general mathematics classes. Call and Wiggin each taught the same unit involving linear equations and word problems. The major difference in instructional technique was that Wiggin's experimental group was taught to get meaning from words and translate them into mathematical symbols. This was done in the manner of the teaching of reading rather than that of teaching mathematics. Since Mr. Wiggin was not greatly familiar with methods of teaching mathematics, the researchers felt that if the results in the experimental group were significantly better, this could only further emphasize the importance of the reading factor.

The results did favor the reading instructional techniques used in the experimental group. Even when mathematical aptitude and reading abilities were controlled, the experimental group did better than the control group on a concluding test based on the unit of algebra that had been taught.

Call and Wiggin infer from their data that teaching special reading skills in mathematics has merit; that even good readers have trouble reading word problems; that mathematics teachers are not equipped to teach reading, which might explain some of the difficulty they encounter in teaching mathematics; that disability in reading mathematics does not show up on standard reading tests; and, that mathematics teachers might get better results if they were trained to teach the kind of reading encountered in mathematics.[8]

Call and Wiggin's last inference—that mathematics teachers might get better results if they were trained to teach the kind of reading encountered in mathematics—represents the basic premise of this book. That is, content teachers can more effectively help their students if they themselves understand and can teach the kinds of reading skills needed to cope with the class materials.

Content area teachers at all levels have a dual role: to extend and to develop reading skills. *Extension* implies that skills introduced in the primary grades must be adapted to the more difficult, longer materials encountered at the intermediate and secondary levels. *Development* is related to new skills students need in order to

---

[8]See *The Mathematics Teacher,* 59 (February, 1966), pp. 149-157, for a more complete account of the study.

advance through the curriculum, hence, the term *developmental reading*. It is *not* designed solely for those students who are having difficulties in reading, but for *all* students—even superior ones. This is what distinguishes developmental reading instruction from other types.

The chart which follows provides an overview of the reading and study skills content areas teachers can extend and develop in the course of their teaching. It also provides a structured overview of the content of this workbook.

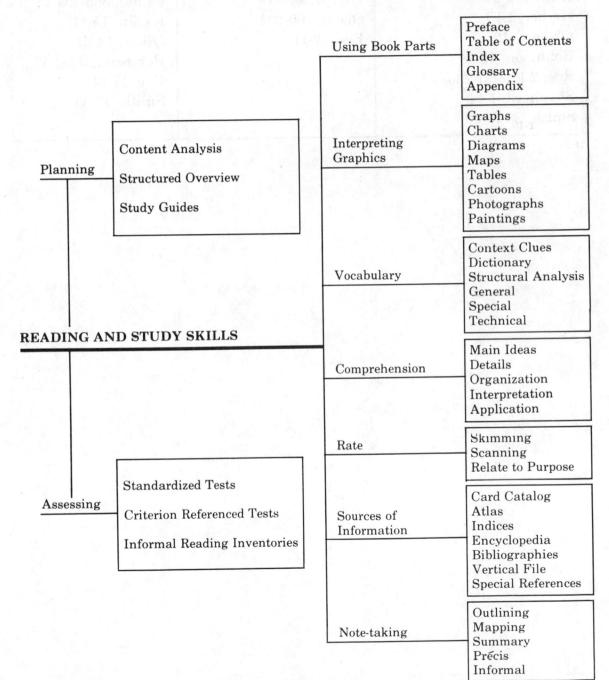

KEY TO TEXTBOOKS—Reading and the Content Teacher

Rationale/Needs/Process	Content Teacher's Role	Programs
Aukerman, 1-8; 19-31	Aukerman, 325-329	Aukerman, 315-324; 113-125
Dechant, 5-8	Burmeister, 343-346	Burmeister, 340-355
Dilner, 8-11	Dilner, 11-15	Dechant, 10-15
Estes, 5-17	Estes, 36-42	Dilner, 365-408
Hafner, 3-56	Herber, 14-36	Karlin, 15-41
Herber, 1-13	Olson, 100-102	Olson, 14-22
Olson, 1-12	Roe, 10-11	Robinson, 335-357
Robinson, 15-28		Roe, 11-14
Roe, 2-10; 221-236		Smith, 75-83
Shepherd, 1-14		
Smith, 28-71		

2

ASSESSING STUDENTS' ABILITY TO READ

READING READINESS

Most teachers think of reading readiness in relation to the teaching of beginning reading in the elementary school. It is true that in the primary grades reading readiness refers to the degree of maturation required before a child is able to read. It is also the name given to activities designed by primary teachers to promote this maturation before formal reading instruction begins.

Reading readiness is an important consideration at other levels of instruction as well. Teachers in the intermediate and secondary grades also need to determine how well students are prepared to read within a content area. Factors that can influence students' reading readiness include: the kind of background they have in the particular content area; previous performance in the content area; the kinds and number of outside interests and obligations; family background; work and travel experience; emotional or physical problems; reading interests; and, of course, how well they read already.

Though many content teachers make it a point to get to know their students through interest surveys, ice-breaking activities, and casual conversation, few find out how well students can read.

Research indicates that content teachers know very little about the reading abilities and needs of their students. Many teachers think that a student's reading level is the same as his grade level. Most teachers soon become aware of students who can't read the textbook once the course gets underway; however, teachers are often amazed to learn that the *range* of reading levels in their classes is approximately equal to the grade level. That is, in a heterogeneously grouped tenth

13

grade class, there are likely to be students reading on every level from third grade through twelfth grade. Moreover, few content teachers test their students to determine reading abilities if an all school testing program does not provide this information. The cliché, "Take the student where he is and move him on," describes the intent of many teachers; however, few employ any means of determining "where the student is" as far as reading is concerned. Testing is a method of assessment that is generally accepted.

TYPES OF READING TESTS

Once having decided to assess students' reading abilities through testing, the teacher is faced with the task of determining the kind of test to use. There are a variety of types of reading tests. The following should help differentiate the types according to their purposes:

Standardized Survey or Status Tests. Most survey tests have at least two parts—vocabulary and paragraph comprehension. Some also include measures of rate of comprehension, word attack skills, sentence meaning and study skills. Survey tests can be administered by a classroom teacher to a group of students, usually within a class period. Be consciously aware that the scores are *not absolute;* they simply give a *rough estimate* of ability. Many factors may influence a student's performance—sickness, heat, time of day, restriction of time. Therefore, competence is not always being measured. Further, these tests will *not* provide an analysis of the types of reading problems students might have, nor their ability to read or perform within a content area. They simply give an estimate of reading age or reading grade level.

Diagnostic Tests. These are designed to give a more *detailed analysis* of silent and oral reading problems. Many sub-tests are therefore included. Usually, diagnostic tests are given by reading specialists to individuals under controlled conditions, and they may take several days to administer and several more to interpret. Based on the analysis of the results, the reading specialist then decides which areas need remediating. Any student who scores two years or more below grade level on a survey test should be referred to a reading specialist for diagnostic testing.

Intermediate Appraisal or Placement Tests. Developed by commercial publishers of reading materials, these tests are used to place students in the company's materials. They should not be used for any other purpose.

14

Informal Reading Inventories. Teacher-made, these tests are based on the textbook and other reading material used in the content area to determine students' abilities to read in that content area. (See Chapter 8 for instructions on how to construct an informal reading inventory.)

USES OF STANDARDIZED TESTS

Scores on standardized tests might be used to obtain an initial basis upon which to form groups within a class. They may indicate some guidelines for selecting materials of appropriate difficulty. They might indicate the types of assignments students can handle and general areas in which they may need instruction and practice. Even though a score on a norm-referenced test is only one possible measure (a profile obtained from an informal reading inventory might be another), it can provide a place to begin learning about students' reading performance.

Also, by examining several different reading tests, a content teacher can gain a notion of the variety of methods used to test reading ability.

SELECTED LIST OF SURVEY TESTS

In most cases, the only type of standardized reading test content area teachers will be concerned with is the survey test. Many good ones are on the market today, so it can be quite a task to select an appropriate test. No one test can be designated here as the "best," but the following are commonly used:

California Achievement Tests. Monterey, CA: California Test Bureau, 1970. (Grades 9-14) Separate reading, arithmetic, and language tests. Provide grade placement scores in vocabulary in content areas, reading comprehension, and reference skills.

Davis Reading Test. New York: Psychological Corporation, 1962. (Grades 8-13) Measures comprehension level and speed of reading.

Diagnostic Reading Tests. Chicago: Committee on Diagnostic Reading Tests, Inc., Science Research Associates, Inc., 1966. (Grades 7-13) Though the name of the tests include the word "diagnostic," these are survey tests which have four sections: survey, vocabulary in specific fields, comprehension, rate of reading and word attack.

Gates-MacGinite Reading Tests. Survey E & F. New York: Teachers College Press, Columbia University, 1970. (Grades 7-12) Sections on speed, vocabulary and comprehension.

Iowa Silent Reading Tests. New York: Harcourt, Brace and Jovanovich, Inc., 1973. Ranges from elementary (Grades 4-8) to advanced (Grades 9-13). Many sub-sections to test rate, comprehension, paragraph comprehension, word meaning, sentence meaning and study skills.

Metropolitan Achievement Tests—Reading. New York: Harcourt, Brace and Jovanovich, Inc., 1970. (Grades 7-9) Tests comprehension and vocabulary.

Nelson-Denny Reading Test. Hopewell, NJ: Houghton-Mifflin, 1973 (Grades 9-16 and adult) Measures for vocabulary, comprehension, and rate.

SRA Achievement Series. Chicago: Science Research Associates, 1963. (Grades 1-9) Tests comprehension, vocabulary, and work-study skills.

Sequential Tests of Educational Progress: Reading (STEP). Princeton, NJ: Cooperative Test Division, Educational Testing Service, 1969. (Grades 7-14) Grade level and percentile norms in five areas of reading comprehension.

Stanford Diagnostic Reading Test. New York: Harcourt, Brace, and Jovanovich, 1973. (Grades 4.5-8.5) Tests literal and inferential comprehension, vocabulary, syllabication, auditory skills, phonic analysis, and rate.

Traxler High School Reading Tests. Indianapolis: Bobbs-Merrill Company, Inc., 1967. (Grades 10-12) Reading rate, story comprehension, main ideas, total comprehension.

REVIEW OF TESTING TERMS

In order to review standardized reading tests intelligently and to interpret the results accurately, it is necessary to understand basic testing terms:

MEAN	The average score; equal to the sum of scores divided by the number of examinees.
MEDIAN	The mid-point; half the scores will be above the median, half below.

STANDARDIZATION

A test becomes standardized after it has been tried out on very large groups of students at the appropriate grade levels in various types of schools throughout the country. This national sample of thousands of students must represent a cross-section of the national population. The scores from this vast "testing of the test" are then used to develop comparative data, or "norms," or averages. Test publishers usually include this data in the form of a table which describes the national average scores of students of the same age or in the same grade. Sometimes sub-group norms are provided for additional interpretation—private school norms, large cities, rural areas, sex, etc. A teacher, then, can compare how students in a particular class did on a test as compared with the national average or a special sub-group.

KINDS OF NORMS

Reading Grade Equivalent. The *median* score for each grade, usually given in terms of years and tenths of years since there are ten months in a school year. For example, a score of 9.3 would be read as ninth grade, third month.

Reading Age. The *median* score based on the age of the student rather than on his grade position, usually expressed in years and twelfths. For example, a student whose chronological age is 16-5 might have a *reading* age of 10-2, meaning that his score is equal to the median score of children who are ten years, two months of age.

Percentiles. Ways of stating how a student compares with other students his own age or in the same grade. If a student has a percentile score of 75, that means that he did *better* than 75 percent of the students with whom he is being compared.

Stanines. The total range of scores is divided into nine levels. Each of the nine levels contains one-half standard deviation. Hence, the term "stanine" which is a contraction of standard nine. In a normal distribution of scores, the fifth stanine straddles the mean. Stanines 1, 2 and 3 are considered below average; stanines 7, 8, and 9 are above average.

RELIABILITY

The degree to which the test gives consistent results. It is usually stated in two ways:

Coefficient of Self-Correlation. A means of expressing how well two forms of the same test compare with each other based on the performance of the students taking the test. If a test has a self-correlation of .90, that means that 90 times out of 100 it will give consistent results. Therefore it is highly reliable.

Standard Error. An estimate of the *amount of change* to be expected when students are retested with an equivalent form. If the standard error is four months, a majority of the students will obtain scores within four months of their first scores. For example, if a student scored 10.3 on the first form of the test and 10.7 (or, 9.9) on the second, the change of score does not necessarily designate a change in the student's ability; it might be attributed to the standard error.

VALIDITY

The degree of accuracy with which a test measures what it is intended to measure.

LIMITATIONS OF STANDARDIZED TESTS

Standardized reading tests have been severely criticized in recent years. Most of the criticism has been in regard to validity. Thomas Newkirk, for example, has listed seven limitations of standardized reading tests which point up weaknesses in validity. He has cited research to support each of his claims. This is his list:

1. Any standardized test is only a measure of performance at one time. . . .To regard a 45-60 minute test as a definitive measure of reading achievement is to ignore the volatility of many secondary students.
2. A standardized reading test purports to measure the student's reading ability by having him read passages which may be of no interest to him. . . .Students read better when the material interests them.
3. The type of reading comprehension measured on reading tests is not the type of comprehension needed for most kinds of reading. . . .The skills needed to comprehend longer

units, book chapters, essays, short stories, are quite different from those tested on standardized reading tests.

4. The rigid time restrictions create an unrealistic environment for the testing of reading....Not only do timed readings create unrealistic pressures, they can penalize good reading habits— reading for style, re-reading, and pausing to think.
5. Tests of reading comprehension tend to over-emphasize factual recall of relatively insignificant facts.
6. Because of standardized procedures, many standardized reading tests may be inappropriate for low socioeconomic and minority groups.
7. Reading tests may actually test pre-existing knowledge as much as they test reading comprehension.[1]

Although standardized reading tests do have their limitations, educators still want and need information upon which to base instructional programs. Because there are so many problems with standardized tests, teachers may refuse to use those which are shown to be invalid or those which would be invalid when used with a particular group. They can insist on better tests, or on tests which are needed to evaluate a particular goup. Apparently, however, this is not a major concern of many teachers and other test users. In his preface to the *Sixth Mental Measurements Yearbook,* Oscar Buros noted:

> Unfortunately, the rank and file of test users do not appear to be particularly alarmed that so many tests are either severely criticized or described as having no validity. Although most test users would probably agree that many tests are either worthless or mis-used, they continue to have the utmost faith in their own particular choice and use of tests regardless of the absence of supporting research or even of the presence of negating research. When I initiated this test reviewing service in 1938, I was confident that frankly critical reviews by competent specialists representing a wide variety of viewpoints would make it unprofitable to publish tests of unknown or questionable validity. Now 27 years later and five *Mental Measurements Yearbooks* later, I realize that I was too optimistic (pp. xxiii—xxiv).

ABUSES OF TESTS

As Buros suggests, standardized tests are often misused. Sometimes teachers are not sure what the test purports to measure and may, therefore, misinterpret the scores. Test results may be unreliable because the administrator did not read and follow directions carefully. Even computers have been known to err. But, even if the test is valid, correctly administered and accurately scored and interpreted, it is not enough to be satisfied with the information that Tommy reads on the second grade level. An examination of sub-test scores may reveal strengths and weaknesses that otherwise might have been overlooked. Sometimes a student obtains a very low

---

[1]Thomas Newkirk, "The Limitations of the Standardized Reading Test," *English Journal,* 64 (March, 1975), pp. 50-52.

score in testing, yet performs well in the classroom. It is not necessary to assume that the test is correct and that the student "had everyone fooled." Teachers, especially new ones, may question their own observation of student performance if it conflicts with the "authority" of a test score.

Tests are often given in school-wide programs to provide information to teachers and others concerned in the education of the student body. If this information is merely added to cumulative folders and not referred to again, then the program will have been expensive, time-consuming, and useless. However, this is not usually the case. Often, a guidance counselor or other agent of the school provides teachers with reading test scores. Teachers should examine the test and its manual so they can determine what the scores "mean." In reviewing the test, they may notice directions that are not clear or seem hard to follow. Attention should be paid to the format of the test and answer sheet as these are sometimes confusing to students. It has happened that answer sheets have been marked vertically rather than horizontally, as indicated (or vice versa) and low scores have resulted. Sometimes the divisions of parts of a test are not clear on the answer sheet and this, also, may cause mismarking. The print may be quite small; the ink color may be distracting or tiring to the eyes. Teachers should analyze the contents of the test to get some idea of the kinds of words used to determine students' general vocabulary. The type of vocabulary skills tested should be noted. It would be wise to examine the passages in the comprehension section. Some selections may have become dated. For example, one test (now revised), included a passage about "the war". The reference was to World War II, yet the test was still being used at a time when many students understood "the war" to mean the war in Viet Nam. Such lapses are bound to occur from time to time. They should be noticed and taken into consideration.

CRITERION REFERENCED TESTS

Because of the validity problems inherent in norm referenced, standardized tests, many educators suggest that criterion referenced tests be used. Criterion referenced tests are not designed to compare a student's performance with a group as norm referenced tests are. They are designed to determine whether a student can do a specific task. Can Tom run a mile in less than four minutes? Can Jane type 65 words per minute for a period of five minutes with no more than five errors? The purpose is not to compare Tom's running with Jane's, nor John's typing with Sue's, but to ascertain whether Tom and John can perform the tasks. Each task has specified criteria.

In criterion referenced tests, the validity of the test seems to be a matter of "common sense validity." If the objective is to run a mile in less than four minutes, then the test is obviously valid if it requires the student to run a mile in less than four minutes. A true-false or matching test on the mechanics of running would not be valid. Criterion referenced tests are more frequently used to test a process or a product than to test verbal ability.

Some norm referenced tests can be used to provide criterion referenced scores. In order to use a standardized test as a criterion referenced test, someone must decide that mastery will be demonstrated by correct responses to a certain number of items. For example, the publisher might say that if a student answers 75 questions out of 100 on a particular test of mathematics skills, he thereby demonstrates mastery of those skills. The score is *not* used to *compare* one student's mathematical skill with that of another student. Many test publishers are now providing both norm referenced and criterion referenced scores to accompany their tests.

KEY TO TEXTBOOKS — ASSESSMENT/TESTING/ EVALUATION

Background	Causes of Reading Problems	Standardized Tests
Aukerman, 9-11 Burmeister, 43 Dechant, 339-346 Garland, 304-313 Herber, 234-254 Karlin, 65-68 Olson, 22-24 Shepherd, 15-19 Smith, 108-134; 417-443	Burmeister, 12-25 Dechant, 8-10; 37-107 Karlin, 303-326 Roe, 17-41	Aukerman, 12-17 Burmeister, 44-46 Dilner, 91-95 Estes, 49-57 Garland, 314-325 Hafner, 67-72 Karlin, 68-83 Olson, 24-29 Robinson, 32-36 Shepherd, 19-21 Smith, 134-136
Criterion Referenced	Attitudes/Interests	Lists of Commercial Tests
Garland, 327-329 Smith, 136-137	Burmeister, 65-90 Estes, 58-65 Olson, 164-168 Smith, 84-92	Aukerman, 13-14 Burmeister, 61-63 Dechant, 346-347; 354-357 Karlin 335-336 Roe, 420-423 Shepherd, 21-23

NATURE OF THE ACTIVITY

In order for content area teachers to become familiar with the possible uses of a standardized reading test (or any commercial test, for that matter) and to prevent misuse of the test itself or of the information it can provide, the test and its accompanying manual should be carefully reviewed. It is important to understand what the test is designed to measure (pertinent to validity). Test items should be examined to see *how* the test is measuring. Often, the manuals which accompany standardized tests do not have enough to say about validity. They do give explanations, often extended ones, about reliability, but the author's word need not be accepted at face value. There are sources to check to learn what professional reviewers have found regarding reliability and validity and to note how they evaluate the test in general. Two of the best sources for this kind of information are Oscar Buros' *Reading Tests and Reviews* and his *Mental Measurements Yearbooks*. These are standard reference books found in most libraries. If the test is new or has been revised since the latest Buros book, then reviews may be sought in professional journals, such as, *Journal of Educational Measurement*.

ACTIVITY

Select a standardized survey reading test for review. Evaluate the test on the Test Review Form.

Exercise 1:   Name _____
Test Review

Name of test _____

Author _____ **Publisher** _____

Copyright Date _____ **Grades** _____

Number of Forms _____

Cost of Class Set: Test _____ Answer Sheets _____

Designed to Measure: _____

Total Time required to give test: _____

Methods of Scoring Available:
     Hand _____ Stencil Key _____ Machine _____ Other _____
Scores Reported in Terms of: raw scores _____ grade level, _____
reading age _____ percentile bands _____ stanines _____ other
Materials Needed for Administering and Scoring:

Standard Error: _____ How is S.E. reported? *(raw scores, percentiles,)*

_____

Reliability: (Many tests report these for individual grade levels being tested and for each section of the test rather than for all grades for the entire test. If so, choose a grade level and report figures given for that particular level.)

_____

Validity: (Usually in statement form in the manual. What have reviewers said about this test's validity?)

Standardization of Population:

Number of students used _____ Number of states or geographical regions represented _____ Size of school districts used ____ _____ Other information _____

Is this sample adequate and representative in your opinion? _____

Directions and Format:

Did you find the directions for administering the test clear? (Yes, No, Explain) _____

Are the directions for scoring the test clear? _____

Are the directions for interpreting the scores clear? _____

Are the directions on the test clear enough for students to follow? _____

_____

Is the format confusing or distracting? _____

Vocabulary Section:

Number of items: _____ Time provided: _____

Describe the methods of testing employed: (synonyms, antonyms, context clues, etc.)

General impression:

Comprehension Section:

Number of Items: _____ Time provided: _____

Are the selections well-chosen in terms of interest and variety of styles represented?

Are the questions "passage-dependent" or could many be answered without reference to the passage?

Are there questions which require the student to go beyond the literal level, i.e., do some questions require the reader to make inferences, draw conclusions, follow sequence?

Are the answers free of ambiguity?

Other comments:

Other Sections: (Following the format above, describe and analyze other sections of the test if provided)

Professional reviewers' comments (from Buros or other sources):

3

ESTIMATING READABILITY

RATIONALE

Despite the abundance of new educational media and materials, the textbook is still the primary learning resource in most courses. In some cases several books may be required. Since no two texts are alike, the student is continually faced with problems of understanding.

Every textbook presents three basic problems. One is the problem of understanding the content itself. The second problem arises in regard to purposes the teacher establishes for reading the material. Third is the question of readability since a text's difficulty is not necessarily commensurate with the grade level in which it is used. Can it be said that an eleventh grade physics book is less difficult to read than a twelfth grade chemistry book? Is an American literature book easier to read than a British literature text? Is algebra simpler to read than geometry? The authors of such books are usually experts in their fields, but seldom are they aware of the reading skills students must possess in order to comprehend the written material. In most cases, they do not consciously control the introduction of new vocabulary and new concepts, nor govern the complexity of sentence structure. At the primary grade levels, these matters are carefully controlled.

Teachers need to gain an awareness of the reading grade level of texts required in their classes. Such an awareness, combined with sound knowledge of students' abilities and of subject matter, will enable teachers to make wise selections and good use of texts and supplemental materials. Some materials may be chosen which are more challenging than the general text; some may be needed that are more simply written, though still at a high interest level. Perhaps some rewriting of materials by the teacher may be indicated. In this way, reading level of texts may

27

be more accurately matched to the reading levels of students, thus accommodating the wide range of reading ability that is often found even in a single class.

READABILITY FORMULAS

In general, the authors of readability formulas have attempted to identify factors that make materials difficult to read. Most agree that factors causing the greatest difficulty are *vocabulary* and *sentence length*, with vocabulary being the most significant determinant of reading comprehension. This word recognition variable has been investigated and quantified in a number of ways including length of words, frequency in the language, and familiarity. In order to quantify this variable, word counts—whether measured by number of letters, syllables, frequency of appearance, or recognizability—have been firmly established as a valid measure.

Measurements of other aspects of vocabulary that probably affect the comprehensibility of materials have not been well developed. Many researchers have investigated the influences of variations in meaning, difficulty and abstractness, but none have successfully incorporated these factors into a formula.

The second major variable in most readability formulas is sentence length. This variable, too, has been shown to be a reliable and valid predictor of reading difficulty. As sentence length increases, the structure usually becomes more complex linguistically, ideas become more dense and more qualified, and the reader is required to "keep track" of the development of an idea for a longer period of time and over a greater span of print. This taxes the memory. It becomes more difficult to relate one aspect of an idea to another.

Sentence structure has been examined as a predictor of readability and has been incorporated into some readability formulas. Some formulas have counted the number of prepositional phrases, while others have considered the number of clauses.

Researchers in the area of readability have become somewhat discouraged as they have come to realize that the relationship between linguistic features and readability is even more complex than was previously thought. Simple shifts in sentence components, for example, can confuse lower ability students even though the same words are used and the ideas are rather simple. An eighth-grade English class of low ability students was observed by the author in which the teacher had developed a simple comprehension exercise based on sentences like: "I read the book *after* I sat down." The teacher asked: "What did I do first, sit down or read the book?" Many of the students said that she read the book first. When the example was changed to: "*After* I sat down, I read the book," most students answered correctly that she sat down first. Several similar sentences were used in which time referenced words were shifted within the sentence. It became obvious that whichever action appeared first in the sentence was most apt to be selected as having happened first regardless of the meaning indicated by the words themselves.

Another factor affecting readability is the *concept load* of the material. Idea density, that is, the number of ideas presented within a set number of words, seems to add to the difficulty of the material. Abstractness of concepts also increases difficulty. For example, a ninth-grade science book may have a ninth-grade readability level as measured by formula. Information may be presented in relatively simple terms in short sentences, yet the sentences may present fact after fact after fact in a short space. The high density of ideas may make the material much more difficult than is quantitatively represented in a readability check. For this reason, it is almost impossible to do a readability measure with accuracy in fields like literature or mathematics. In literature, a poem may seem short and simple, but the symbolic elements, the influence of form on meaning, and the intricate linguistic patterns often render it difficult to read and *interpret*. Likewise, many verbal problems in mathematics are short, often only a sentence or two. To read these problems with enough understanding so that they can be converted into mathematical equations is where the difficulty lies. Each word, even punctuation, is important and may represent a difficult mathematical concept.

Although readability is influenced by abstractness of words, number and difficulty of concepts, organization and format of the text, as well as interests, experiences and purposes of the reader, these elements cannot be incorporated into a formula. The goal in developing readability formulas has been to obtain the highest degree of prediction using the least number of factors. As a result, readability scores are approximations.

Several readability formulas are available. Among the better known are the Dale-Chall, Flesch, and Spache. Because of its brevity, simplicity and comparable accuracy, the Fry Readability Graph is often used by the content area teacher.

READING LEVELS

Another way the reading difficulty of material can be described is in terms of how difficult a particular book is to a particular person. This description of reading levels is based upon observation rather than quantification.

It has been said that everyone is ignorant, but about different things. Every person probably has a **frustration level** in reading. As an illustration, suppose that a "good" reader—one who has performed at the college level on a standardized reading test—were to attempt to read a medical textbook on surgical procedures. Without the necessary background upon which to base the information, this person is likely to be unable to comprehend vocabulary (perhaps to be unable even to pronounce terms easily). Comprehension of the processes described is likely to be sketchy. Recall will be difficult. This person can be said to be operating at the frustration level.

Another level has been termed the **instructional level.** This can be described as the level at which one can read well enough to get main ideas and recall them after reading the material. The reader can pronounce most of the words in the selection, but will need help in some cases. In other words, with some help—with instruction from the teacher—the material can be read.

A third level is called the **independent level.** The reader has no difficulty at all. Recall is complete, understanding is sound, few words cause difficulty in pronunciation or meaning.

All readers read on all three levels depending upon the type of information and the manner in which it is presented. An idea simple enough for an average sixth grader to understand could be explained using a difficult vocabulary and a difficult style so that it would take an average twelfth grader to understand it. Or, a complex idea that ordinarily would be understood by a twelfth grader might be rewritten using simpler vocabulary and simpler style so that a ninth grader could understand it.

In a recent unpublished master's study, Carter (1977) found that when sixth grade children who read on the twelfth grade level as measured by the *Gates-McGinite Test* were given materials written on that level about a subject in which they had an expressed interest, they could not adequately answer questions about the material. Carter inferred that the students' concept development was not at as high a level as their measured skill level which caused them to become frustrated.[1]

Understanding these reading levels can be of help to a classroom teacher. Often a student's score on a standardized test represents his *frustration level*, the point where his reading skills break down. Therefore, classroom or instructional materials should be written below that grade level. If students are expected to do independent, individualized work, then it is of great importance that the material they are to work with is written below the level indicated by their reading grade score.

---

[1]Carole Carter, "The Relationship between Reading Interest and Reading Comprehension of Sixth Grade Students" (Master's thesis, College of Education, Florida Technological University, 1977).

THE FRY READABILITY GRAPH[2]

GRAPH FOR ESTIMATING READABILITY —EXTENDED
by Edward Fry, Rutgers University Reading Center, New Brunswick, N.J. 08904

Average number of syllables per 100 words

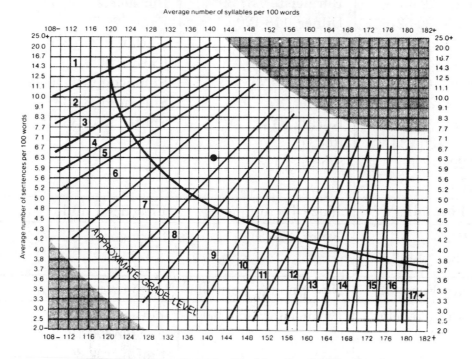

Expanded Directions for Working Readability Graph

1. Randomly select three (3) sample passages and count out exactly 100 words each, beginning with the beginning of a sentence. Do count proper nouns, initializations, and numerals.
2. Count the number of sentences in the hundred words, estimating length of the fraction of the last sentence to the nearest one-tenth.
3. Count the total number of syllables in the 100-word passage. If you don't have a hand counter available, an easy way is to simply put a mark above every syllable over one in each word, then when you get to the end of the passage, count the number of marks and add 100. Small calculators can also be used as counters by pushing numeral 1, then push the + sign for each word or syllable when counting.
4. Enter graph with *average* sentence length and *average* number of syllables; plot dot where the two lines intersect. Area where dot is plotted will give you the approximate grade level.
5. If a great deal of variability is found in syllable count or sentence count, putting more samples into the average is desirable.
6. A word is defined as a group of symbols with a space on either side; thus, *Joe, IRA, 1945,* and & are each one word.
7. A syllable is defined as a phonetic syllable. Generally, there are as many syllables as vowel sounds. For example, *stopped* is one syllable and *wanted* is two syllables. When counting syllables for numerals and initializations, count one syllable for each symbol. For example, *1945* is four syllables, *IRA* is three syllables, and & is one syllable.

Note: This "extended graph" does not outmode or render the earlier (1968) version inoperative or inaccurate; it is an extension. (REPRODUCTION PERMITTED—NO COPYRIGHT)

---

[2]Edward Fry, "Fry's Readability Graph: Clarifications, Validity, and Extension to Level 17," *Journal of Reading, 21* (December, 1977), p. 249.

KEY TO TEXTBOOKS—Readability

Background	Fry Graph (1968)	Cloze Procedure
Aukerman, 19-45 Burmeister, 30-32 Dilner, 61-62; 120-132 Estes, 18-23 Forgan, 14-16 Garland, 272-274 Hafner, 86 Robinson, 130-133 Roe, 42-29 Smith, 7-12	Burmeister, 37-39* Dilner, 118-120 Estes, 23-24 Forgan, 17-38 Garland, 275 Hafner, 87 Karlin, 94 Roe, 48 Smith, 10	Burmeister, 55-59 Estes, 29-32 Garland, 275-276 Karlin, 91-93 Robinson, 131; 40-42; 106-109 Shepherd, 37-38 Smith, 137-138; 158
SMOG Formula	Maze Technique	Flesch Formula
Estes, 25-27 Hafner, 88	Estes, 32-33	Burmeister, 32-37
Dale-Chall Formula	New Spache Formula	Adapting Materials
Burmeister, 357-358	Burmeister, 359-360	Forgan, 49-64 Forgan, 70-73 Smith, 15-23

*1977 Fry Graph

ACTIVITY

Using the Fry Graph for Estimating Readability, determine the approximate grade level of a textbook of your choice. (Keep in mind that this is a rough estimate and does not measure conceptual difficulty.)

Exercise 2:
READABILITY

Name _____

Title of Textbook _____

Authors/Editors _____

Copyright Date _____ Edition _____

Publisher _____

Course title in which text is used _____

Grade level(s) at which text is used _____

	Sentences/100 words	Syllables/100 words
1st 100 word sample p. _____.	_____	_____
2nd 100 word sample p. _____.	_____	_____
3rd 100 word sample p. _____.	_____	_____
Totals	_____	_____
Divide totals by 3	_____	_____

Plot these results on the Fry Graph.

Readability Level _____

Is this textbook one of a series?* _____

Is the entire series used in your school?* _____

*If the book is one in a series and the entire series is not used, concepts which have been introduced in earlier volumes are assumed in later ones. Thus, if a text is used "out of series," the teacher may have to compensate for gaps which are apparent.

4

USING BOOK PARTS

RATIONALE

Because textbooks in the various disciplines have certain parts in common, teachers often falsely assume that students are adept in using tables of contents, indices, appendices, glossaries, and other such aids. Unfortunately, many students are not proficient. Some students can handle a textbook daily and not be aware that it even *has* a glossary, much less use it.

Even if students know how to use book parts in general, these basic parts may have been given special functions in a specific textbook. For example, *Biological Science: Molecules to Man,* the Blue Version by the Biological Sciences Curriculum Study Committee (Houghton-Mifflin, 1968) has no glossary. The authors have incorporated the meanings of words within the text material. The student must pay attention to the style and/or color of typeface used in presenting these definitions because concepts, theories and terms are printed in blue boldface type; special biological vocabulary words are printed in italic boldface type; scientific names of organisms are italicized. Since there is no glossary, if a student wishes to look up a particular term, he must use the index. In the index, the style of typeface of the numerals indicates different kinds of information. Small numerals in boldface refer to pages on which terms are defined or explained, while numerals in italic boldface refer to pages with illustrations.

If the student has not bothered to read the preface (and few of them do), or, if the teacher has not pointed out these unique features, the student may have a difficult time discovering how and where to look for meanings of words in this particular book.

From this one example, it can be seen that it is the responsibility of the teacher of each subject at each grade level to help students learn the parts and unique features of the text to be used in the course.

NATURE OF THE ACTIVITY

It seems logical that the best time to introduce students to the textbook is the day that it is issued. This can be done in several ways. It can be done orally by going through the text asking both simple and complex questions on each book part, orienting the questions toward problem-solving.

Again, using the BSCS Blue Version biology book as an example, suppose the teacher wishes to formulate questions to evaluate how well students can use the index. A sample question might be, "Find an illustration of the human brain and give the name of the part of the brain which controls balance and posture."

This question involves several steps in finding the answer. First, the student will have to decide whether to look under *H* for *Human* with the sublisting *brain,* or under *B* for *Brain* with the sublisting *human.* After finding the listing, he will next have to determine which page number given is the one that indicates an illustration. (Remember, the discriminating factor is the style of print used.) Then he will have to turn to the page in the text, find the correct illustration (there are two pictures of the human brain on the same page), read the diagram of the brain to find the part labeled: *Cerebellum: balance and vision.* In this one relatively simple question, the student has had to use indexing skills, cross-referencing skills, locational skills, and diagram-reading skills to find the answer.

Another way to discover how well students can use book parts is to construct a series of written exercises. These do not have to be simple question/answer type like, "On what page does the short story, 'The Lottery,' begin?" Many can be in this form; however, older students often are not motivated by this type of activity. You may have to exercise your ingenuity in devising clever, interesting questions in order to hold the attention of these pupils.

There follows a series of examples from various content areas and on different grade levels. The first series of exercises is based upon a fifth grade social studies text by McVicar and Hardy, entitled, *People in America,* (Addison-Wesley Publishing Co., 1973). Notice that brief explanations regarding the purpose of each book part have been incorporated into the exercises.

Sample Exercises: Using Book Parts
Social Studies

How is a book like a person?
A person has many different body parts. Books have parts, too. When a person is

functioning best, the various body parts are working together in harmony: eyes show fingers how to pick up a needle or a sledge hammer, ears signal feet to hurry out of the way of an oncoming truck or to move in time with the music. To get the best use out of ourselves, we use ALL of our bodies, not just our torsos. The torso is where most of the body processes are going on, but it must be supported and given "meaning" by the appendages—head, arms and legs.

In order to get the most from your textbooks, learn how to use ALL of their parts. Each book is different. This exercise is based on our social studies text, but other books can be examined in much the same way.

Directions: Study each part of the book as it is taken up. A series of questions or problems will be given for you to answer.

A. **The Cover.** Look at the front, the back and the spine.
1. What is the title of this book?   *People in America*
2. Who publishes the book?   *Addison-Wesley Publishing Co.*
3. What is the picture? (Tell how it seems to be related to the title).
   a big city, maybe Chicago, lots of people, Americans, live there.

(There is another piece of information on the cover that doesn't seem to have much meaning right now. Keep "Taba Program" in mind. Maybe it will pop up somewhere else.)

B. **Title Page and Credits.** Sometimes there is a **Preface,** too, to give you some more information about the book and its purpose.
1. Besides the title, the authors' names are on the title page. The title page is colored green. Who are the authors?
   K. McVicar and P. Hardy
2. What kind of jobs do they have besides writing books?
   professors at universities in California
3. Look at the back (the "verso") of the title page.
   a) Tell something about Hilda Taba.   *innovative & perceptive teacher*
   b) Would it be all right to take some photographs from this book and copy them to use in our school literary magazine?   *no*
   c) What would you do if you really wanted to do this?   *get permission*
4. This book is filled with photographs paintings, etc. There is an interesting lithograph on page 266 in the chapter called "Americans Divided."
   a) Look in the "Photographic Acknowledgements" (just next to the verso of the title page) and find out where the picture came from.
      Library of Congress
   b) If you had a friend who was very interested in the Pueblo Indians, you might want to find out where the map, titled "Land of the Pueblos" on page 103 came from. If it came from a book, that book might be a perfect gift for your friend's birthday. Look in the section called "Map Acknowledgements" to see where the map came from Who is the publisher?
      University of Oklahoma Press

C. **Table of Contents:** Turning from the **Credits** you find a double page spread called "Contents." The book is divided into large parts which are then divided into smaller parts.
1. How can you tell which are the large parts (the units)?
   Big print across top of pages
2. Which are the smaller parts (the chapters) in the unit called, "Americans in Revolt?
   Independence from Great Britian, and Independence from Spain
3. How many pages are in this unit?   *(238 minus 209 equals 29 pages)*
4. How is the first unit of the book going to be presented? (Read the chapter titles and see what they have in common.)
   They are all about families, from various ethnic groups

5. What do you think is the general subject of the chapter called, "Americans Divided?"
    Civil War
6. If you want to find out something about life as it is today in the United States, what two units would be of most interest to you? *the first and the last*
7. Does the Glossary come before or after the Index? *before*
8. What is the last thing in this book? *the Index*

D. **The Body of the Text:**
1. There is a map on page 148. What is the title? *Spain 17th Century*
2. How can you tell which city is the capital if you don't already know?
    The box at the bottom tells me that the national capital is marked with a star in a circle.
3. About how far is it across the Strait of Gibraltar between Spain and Africa?
    about 10 miles according to the Scale of Miles
4. Did the Balearic Islands belong to Spain or to France? *Spain*
    How could you tell? *because of the color*
5. What was the relationship of Portugal to Spain in the 17th Century?
    It was a province—it's purple and has "province" lines to mark its boundary.
6. When did the 17th century begin and when did it end?
    (If you don't know, you might scan the pages of the chapter looking for dates that might give you a hint, at least.) *1600 to 1700*

E. **The Glossary:**
1. Look at page 465, up at the top, under the word "Glossary." What information are you given there?
    a) *Use like a dictionary*
    b) *Although some words have other meanings,*
    c) *Only the meaning important to this book is given in the glossary.*
2. What word is between the words *international* and *laboratory*? *justice*
3. Can you find *kibbutz* in the glossary? *no*
4. Does the glossary tell you how to pronounce *unanimous*? *no*
5. What does *immigration* mean? *coming into another country to live*
    Will the glossary help you to find out more about it? *no*

F. **The Index:**
1. There are many entries in this Index. What do the numbers after each entry mean?
    page numbers to find information
2. How is the Index arranged so that you can find things quickly?
    alphabetically
3. Will the Index help you find out more about immigration? *yes*
    What are your choices? *from Mexico, in New York, World War I and . . .*
    Who were some of the immigrants who came to New York? *the Jews*
4. Using the Index, you should be able to find at least 16 places in the book where something is said about the way people are educated or have been educated in the United States. Tell how you do it. *there are cross references at "education" and at "schools".*
5. Use the Index to locate information about Chicanos. Read a little about them from the text. Have you noticed any way in which this book seems different from other social studies books? If so, how is it different? *personal narrative approach*

G. Do you like this book? _____ Why? _____

To illustrate the variety of forms these exercises may take, here are two examples of exercises based on tables of contents. The first one is based on a fifth-grade mathematics text entitled, *Mathematics for Individual Achievement* by Denhom et al. (Houghton-Mifflin Co., 1974).

Sample Exercise: Using Book Parts
Table of Contents
Mathematics

Directions: Look at the back of the title page in your math book. You will see the table of contents. The numbers on the left are page numbers. The chart below is a sample of the math teacher's lesson plan. Use the information on the chart along with the table of contents. Answer the questions.

Day	GROUP I	GROUP II	GROUP III
Monday	pp. 11-14		Begin place value
Tuesday		Start fractions	
Wednesday	Post-test		Estimates, Rounding
Thursday		p. 29	
Friday	Math Lab		Math Lab

1. How many pages are in Part A? _____ Part B? _____ Part C? _____ Part D? _____
2. A. Which Group will be working on pages 11-14 on Monday? _____
    B. What will they be doing? _____
    C. What day will they be tested? _____
    D. What page is the test on? _____
    E. They will be doing a math lab on Friday. How many math labs are in this Unit? _____
    F. Which one do you think they will be doing? _____
    G. Turn to the math lab and see what extra thing they will need to have. What is it? _____
3. A. Group II is going to begin fractions on Tuesday. What page will they start on? _____
    B. When will they get to page 29? _____
    C. What is on that page? Look and see. _____
4. A. Group III is ready to begin place value on Monday. What page will they turn to? _____
    B. What will they be doing on Wednesday? _____
    C. What pages will they be working on? _____
    D. What math lab will they be doing at the end of the week? _____
    E. What kind of material will the teacher have on hand for them to use? Look at the page and see. _____
5. How is this table on contents different from those of other textbooks you are using? _____
6. In addition to the math labs, what other activity is repeated in every unit? _____

Next is an example of an exercise based on the Table of Contents of *The Dynamics of Language* by Glatthorn, Kriedler, and Heiman (D.C. Heath and Company, 1971):

Sample Exercise: Using Book Parts
Table of Contents
English Language

1. I can tell you about Greek elements in your language. What chapter am I in? _____
2. Two of us are the same length. What chapters are we? _____
3. If you want to know how psychology is involved in communication, look at me! I am chapter _____
4. You have a problem with punctuation? You can rely on me for help. I am page _____
5. Do you want to make a negative statement out of this question? To find out how, look at me, I am chapter _____
6. You say you can never tell the difference between proper and common nouns? I'll help you. I am page _____
7. You haven't the slightest idea what "intonation" is? Tch, tch. Come to me. I'll tell you. I am the _____
8. You are trying to talk your teacher out of a test? Among my pages I have some information on ways of writing convincing arguments. I am chapter _____
9. I am the shortest chapter in the book, but I think I have the nicest sounding name. My title is _____
10. You didn't exactly remember what you read about noun phrases for the last test. We can help you. We are pages _____

In some content areas, certain book parts are used more often than others. In mathematics, for example, the appendices (which are often formulas and tables) are probably used more than the index. In foreign languages, the glossary is probably used more than any other part. Often, the important part has several specialized features and specific information not found in similar parts of texts used in other subjects. In developing exercises on the various book parts, it is therefore important to carefully analyze each part of the text to determine how much and what kind of information is presented while at the same time assessing the relative importance of that part in aiding the student.

Glossaries, for example, vary quite a bit. Some provide merely a definition, while others may include pronunciation guides, derivation information, usage, part of speech, even illustrations. The glossary in *Adventures in English Literature* (Harcourt, Brace & World, 1952), has a variety of features. In the exercise below, notice how the student's attention is directed to these special features.

Sample Exercise: Using Book Parts
Glossary
Literature

1. What is the *literary* definition of "burlesque?"
2. What *usage label* is given to the word "codger?"
3. What *part of speech* is "metaphorically?"
4. How many lines are in a "quatrain?"

5. What does the *prefix* mean in the word "confute?"
6. What symbol is given in the *Pronunciation Key* for the vowel sound in the word "book?"
7. Where did the "Huguenots" live?
8. Write two sentences using different meanings of the word "luminous."
9. What is the *poetic form* of "vermillion?"
10. What *language* does the word "throstle" come from?
11. What is the *noun form* of the word "precocious?"
12. Divide "psychiatry" into *syllables* and mark the *accented* one.
13. Give a *synonym* for "blatant."
14. Write an "epitaph" you would like to have.

In the next sample exercise, knowledge of how the glossary works is essential if students are to use the book efficiently. These questions are based on the *A-LM Spanish, Level One, Second Edition* (Harcourt, Brace and Jovanovich, Inc., 1969).

Sample Exercise: Using Book Parts
Glossary
Spanish Language

1. A glossary may be called a special dictionary of technical or specialized words and terms used within a book. What is the name of the glossary in this book?
   Spanish-English Vocabulary
2. How could you tell that the entry, *aparecer (zc)* is a verb without knowing any Spanish or the English translation of the word?
   According to the introduction to the glossary, the letters in parentheses indicate alternations in **verb** *stems.*
3. Notice that after each definition there is a number or letter-number combination. What do these refer to?
   various places in which to locate the first appearance of the word or phrase. They are codes.
4. What does the abbreviation "f" stand for? *feminine*
5. What does the abbreviation "fn" stand for? *footnote*
6. What does "pp" stand for? *past participle*
7. Explain each part of the following entry:
   "swéater m (swéaters pl) sweater, 12 S (see fn page 224)."

   The Spanish word swéater is a masculine noun whose plural form is written swéaters; it means sweater in English and can be found in 2 places: in Unit 12 in the Supplement on page 224, and also in a footnote on page 224.

Teachers may wish to include some questions regarding the use of book parts in a section in an informal reading inventory. See Chapter 8 for instruction in developing informal reading inventories.

KEY TO TEXTBOOKS—Using Book Parts

General	Preface	Table of Contents
Karlin, 110-111 Olson, 31-36; 44-49	Roe, 188	Karlin, 225-226 Thomas, 258-260 Roe, 188
Index	Glossaries	Appendix
Karlin, 236-228 Thomas, 258-260 Roe, 188-190	Roe, 190	Roe, 190

Also see:

Jewett, Arno. "Using Book Parts," *Developing Study Skills in Secondary Schools. Perspectives in Reading No. 4.* Ed. Harold L. Herber. Newark, Del.: International Reading Association, 1965. 32-41.

ACTIVITY

Using the textbook of your choice, develop at least 10 sample questions on each of the book parts for which an exercise page has been provided. If a particular book part is not included in your text, select examples from supplemental materials in order to complete the exercise. Focus on problem-solving activities. Attempt to construct some exercises and activities which are creative and imaginative to give variety to your approach.

Exercise 3:
BOOK PARTS

Name _____

Preface, Introduction, or Foreword

Table of Contents

44

Name _____

Index (Indices)

Appendix (Appendices)

Glossary

5

EXTENDING VOCABULARY

RATIONALE

In order to read biology, you have to be able to "talk" biology; in order to read math, you have to "talk" math. Each discipline has its own language. Before students can comprehend the "plain sense" of the content—much less make out the subtleties of it—they have to understand the language. As stated in the section on readability, the most significant determinant of reading comprehension is vocabulary.

John S. Simmons has identified three kinds of vocabulary which every teacher is responsible for developing: general, technical, and special. He defines these vocabularies in the following way:

General vocabulary refers to that store of words which each student owns, adds to, and uses in everyday activities of his life. . . .

Technical terms relate directly and usually exclusively to the content area in question. . . .Whatever the area, each teacher is obliged to inventory those technical terms used in his course, to be aware of those introduced at earlier grade levels, and to provide clear, workable definitions for those terms he utilizes in his instructions. . . .

Specialized vocabulary . . . are those words which have a commonly known denoted meaning but which have very different and highly specific definitions when used in the context of a given content area. A mathematics teacher, for example, assigns a definite meaning to the word "radical," which is far different from the equally precise meaning assigned to it by the teacher of social studies.[1]

---

[1]John S. Simmons, "Word Study Skills," *Developing Study Skills in Seconday Schools. Perspectives in Reading No. 4.* Edited by Harold L. Herber. (Newark, Del.: International Reading Association, 1965), p.17.

Vocabulary study should not be a series of isolated lists of words for students to look up in dictionary or glossary, copy the meanings, and use in sentences, the objective being to pass a test on Friday. Rather, it should be an integral part of every reading assignment since the significant terms usually indicate the key concepts to be learned. For this reason, the determination of major concepts and key vocabulary is an important part of the content analysis a teacher does in planning a reading lesson and is the basis of a structured overview to introduce the lesson. (Content analysis and structured overviews will be discussed in Chapter 9.)

TYPES OF VOCABULARY SKILLS

Dictionary and glossary skills are important. These were mentioned in Chapter 4, "Using Book Parts." Other vocabulary skills, however, are just as important. Nevertheless, content area teachers, generally, have given much less attention to these other aspects of vocabulary development.

Most reading teachers agree that the single most important vocabulary skill is the ability to search out word meaning from **clues** given within the **context** that surrounds the word. We acquire vocabulary in this way as little children, and we continue to learn in this fashion as adults—by hearing words used over and over again in similar contexts. For this reason, it is often difficult to give a precise meaning for a word we know. Often, when asked to define a particular word, the response is, "I can't give you a definition, but I can use it in a sentence." The way in which the word is used will give the inquirer some idea of its meaning—again, through context.

The use of context clues to determine meanings of unknown words does have limitations, however. First, the reader has to recognize the fact that the context is providing clues to help him discover the meaning of the unknown word. Second, in order to be helpful, the clues should be near the word (preferably within the same sentence). Third, context can reveal only a partial definition of a word.

Context clues have been categorized in a variety of ways. While it is not necessarily important that students memorize the *label* for each of the context clues described here, it is important that they know how to recognize the actual clues and understand how each reveals meaning. Lee Deighton lists six types of clues: outright definition, examples, modifiers, restatement, inference, and inference through established connections.[2] The following are examples of how each works.

---

[2]See Lee Deighton, *Vocabulary Development in the Classroom* (Columbia University: Teachers College Press, 1965), pp. 6-14.

Outright definition. The usual pattern is linking the unknown word with a form of the verb *be:* "The elementary backstroke *is* a combination arm pull and frog kick."

Examples are frequently used to provide a classification of meaning within a context. Signal words *(like, such as, for example, etc.)* often precede the example: "Substances *like* hydrogen and oxygen, that cannot be changed into component substances, are called elements. Substances *like* water that contain more than one element are compounds."

Modifiers. These may be phrases, clauses, or single words often in the form of predicate adjectives: "In the representation of numbers by letters we may use a subscript, *which is* a small number slightly below and to the right of the letter."

Restatements. These are announced by signal words like *that is to say, that is, in other words, what this means, to put it another way.* A restatement may also be made using *or* followed by a synonym. Sometimes dashes or parentheses indicate a restatement. "The senator from South Carolina was notorious for filibustering, *that is,* making long speeches to delay legislative action."

Inference is the process of gathering details and "reading between the lines" in order to perceive relationships that have not been explicitly stated: "The Russian colossus exercised a spell upon Europe. On the chessboard of military planning, Russia's *size and weight of numbers* represented *the largest piece.*"[3]

Inference through established connections is accomplished primarily through recognizing relationships established by sentence construction—parallel construction, repetition of key words; or the use of connecting words which indicate comparison or contrast: "Mountainous *or* flat, wet *or* arid, land is precious to man."

Exercises to develop skill in using context clues can be designed by lifting from the textbook sentences in which meanings of general, special, or technical words are somehow indicated by context clues. Attempt to find examples of sentences which reveal meanings of words in different ways. Copy the sentence, underline the word to be defined, then design a step-by-step procedure to guide students in analysing the sentence to determine the meaning of the unknown word. This may, of course, be carried out as a class discussion as well as in the form of a written exercise. If you simply provide the sentence with the unknown word underlined and a multiple choice of possible definitions without also providing a step-by-step analysis procedure, you will be testing students, not guiding them.

The following are some sentences from the short story, "The Devil and Tom Walker," in which the definitions of several difficult "general" vocabulary words are revealed through context clues. The questions are given to help guide the students' search for these clues.

---

[3]Barbara W. Tuckman, *The Guns of August* (New York: Macmillan Co., 1962), p. 56.

I. Tom was told of great sums of money buried by Kidd, the pirate, and that all this money was protected so no one could discover it unless he *propitiated* the Devil and gained his favor.
  1. What is the word we are trying to find the meaning of?
    a. pirate   b. protected   c. propitiated
  2. Who protected Kidd's money?
    a. Tom   b. Devil   c. pirate
  3. What two things did someone have to do to discover where Kidd's money was buried?
    a. _____   b. _____
  4. If you had to gain the favor of someone, you would most likely do this by:
    a. lying to him   b. outwitting him   c. pleasing him
  5. A possible meaning of propitiated is:
    a. begged   b. prayed   c. pleased
II. Tom Walker set up as a *usurer* in Boston. Everyone driven to raise money by desperate means and desperate sacrifices hurried to him. He squeezed his customers closer and closer and sent them at length as dry as a sponge from his door.
  1. What did people need from Tom? _____
  2. Why did they *hurry* to him to get it? _____
  3. What did Tom do to his customers? _____
  4. When Tom was through with his customers, they were "squeezed dry like a sponge". What was Tom squeezing from them? _____
  5. Were people better or worse off after Tom was through with them? _____
  6. Is a *usurer* a good guy or a bad guy? _____
  7. A definition of *usurer* could be:
    a. treasurer   b. banker   c. cashier   d. loan shark
III. Tom's wife was a tall *termagant,* fierce of temper, loud of tongue, and strong of arm.
  1. Who is the word *termagant* describing? _____
  2. From this sentence we get a quick character sketch. Which of the following would describe her behavior:
    _____ hot-headed   _____ cool   _____ peaceful
    _____ quarrelsome   _____ boisterous   _____ soft-spoken
  3. A termagant, then, is a:
    a. childless woman   b. loving woman   c. scolding woman

For poor readers or younger students, some basic context exercises of a different nature may be designed. In these, a nonsense word is used in place of a familiar term and sentences are developed which gradually reveal the meaning of the nonsense word. Various types of clues are used that have a cumulative effect. For example:

**Sample Exercise: Context Clues
Basic Mathematics**

1. A *miggle* is a shape. A miggle is a polygon. A miggle has many names. The different kinds of miggles are named by the length of their sides. Some road signs are miggles. A "yield" sign is an upside down miggle. If all sides are equal, it is called an equilateral miggle. If each side is a

different length, it is called a scalene miggle. No matter what the length, all miggles have three sides. A miggle is a _____.
Draw a miggle:

2. A *morpf* is a way of naming a number, or it shows the part of a unit. A morpf is made up of two numbers. One of the numbers of the morpf shows the number of equal parts into which the unit is divided; the other number of the morpf shows the number of equal parts which are taken. The two numbers of the morpf are separated by a horizontal or diagonal line. A morpf may also be used to show the division of one number by another. Different morphs can name the same number. For example 3/6, 4/8, 6/12 are all morpfs which name the number 1/2 (which is also a morpf.) A morpf is a _____
What morpfical part of each drawing is shaded? (The first one is done for you.)

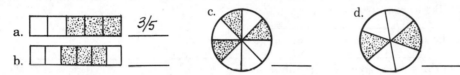

a. 3/5

b. ____

c. ____

d. ____

3. A *sleg* fraction is one in which the bottom number (denominator) is restricted to 10 or any multiple of 10 by itself (10, 100, 1000, etc.). For example, 9/10, 9/100, 39/1,000 are sleg fractions. A sleg fraction can be expressed by using a sleg point, then the number is simply called a sleg. Thus, 9/10 is a sleg fraction, but not a sleg. However, .9 is both a sleg fraction and a sleg. When you have a number which has both a whole number and a sleg, it is called a mixed sleg. For example, 20.9 is a mixed sleg. The sleg point separates the whole number from the sleg fraction. A sleg is a _____.
Change these sleg fractions to slegs:

9/10 = ____.9____   20 91/100 = ___20.91___

6/10 = _____   20 56/100 = _____

8/10 = _____   20 77/1000 = _____

4. Most of you have used *flips* in your math and science classes. Flips are used in business, industry and in the laboratory. Flips are also used at home in cooking, in the workshop, and while banking or shopping. Flips are helpful because they make it easier to do hard problems more quickly. A pilot may use this flip: $d = r t$. A banker uses this flip: $i = p r t$. The flip is a _____.

The flip used by the pilot was $d = r t$, or distance equals rate times time. Anyone who travels can use this flip. Complete the following table using this flip: $d = r t$.

r	50	16	20	850	km/h
t	2	6	3½	10	hours
d	100				km

Context clues are usually helpful, often essential, in determining the meanings of specialized vocabulary words. To know which meaning to assign to words like *union, radical, fold* and *set* depends upon whether the context is social studies, mathematics, home economics, or science. For these specialized words, it is important that students distinguish among the various possible meanings and identify the meaning appropriate to the subject at hand. Here is one way to design such an exercise:

Sample Exercise: Context Clues
Mathematics

Directions:
Many common words take on special meanings when used in mathematics. Also, the same words can mean different things depending on how they are used in a sentence. Below are several groups of sentences. Explain the meanings of the common word in each group.

1. ROOT
   a. The tree had a long root.
   _____
   b. Pigs like to root around in the ground.
   _____
   c. I get hoarse when I root at football games.
   _____
   d. Six is the square root of thirty-six.
   _____

2. SET
   a. My sister has to set the table every night for dinner.
   _____
   b. My mother sets her hair every night.
   _____
   c. Jose is a set designer for MGM.
   _____
   d. A set is a collection of things. Set A $\{2, 4, 6, 8\}$
   _____

3. POWER
   a. We get our power from the hydroelectric plant.
   _____
   b. The President doesn't have much power over the Congress.
   _____
   c. He owns a power boat, a power mower, and a power saw.
   _____
   d. He couldn't solve the problem of finding 9 to the 3rd power.
   _____

4. UNION
   a. The United Auto Workers is a labor union.
   _____
   b. Some people call Russia the Soviet Union.
   _____
   c. My grandfather wears a union suit.
   _____
   d. The union of two sets is a set containing all elements in both sets.
   _____

5. BASE
   a. The base of the pillar was cracked.
   _____
   b. He was stationed at Maxwell Air Force Base.
   _____
   c. The catcher got four base hits in the game.
   _____
   d. We are used to a base ten numbering system.
   _____

Here is another way to write exercises for words which take on specialized meanings when used within the context of a specific subject area. Present the term. Give several definitions and ask students to identify the special way it is used in your subject area.

Sample Exercise: Context Clues
Civics

Directions: Underline each possible meaning of the word once and then underline the civics usage a second time.

1. appointment   a. the naming of a person to fill an office
                          b. an arranged meeting
                          c. to set value on

2. platform   a. a high flat surface, such as a stage for speakers
                          b. the closing of business
                          c. a political party's program

3. customs   a. tax on foreign goods
                          b. practices or traditions common to many
                          c. clothes worn for holidays

Structural analysis, or the analysis of word parts, is another way to unlock approximate meanings of words. A knowledge of prefixes and suffixes is fundamental, especially of those which have fixed meanings. Such prefixes as *anthropo-, auto-, biblio-, homo-, hydro-, photo-, poly-, uni-,* and some eighteen more which Deighton has identified will reveal the meaning of over 200 English words, many of which are technical terms in various discipines.[4] Common noun suffixes like *-archy, -bility, -meter, -ology,* and *-chrome* can unlock the meanings of hundreds more. These prefixes and suffixes when combined with root words produce literally thousands of words, any of which are easily deciphered by one who has an understanding of the separate parts. For example, the prefix *poly-* is found in technical vocabularies in many disciplines: *polychrome* (art), *polyethylene* (chemistry), *polyglot* (linguistics), *polygon* and *polynomial* (mathematics), *polyphonic* (music), *polytheism* (social studies).

Word parts should not be taught simply by giving a list of prefixes and suffixes for students to memorize. Analysis of words parts, like any other skill, should be taught when the need arises. Therefore, when reading the chapter to prepare plans for instruction, vocabulary words that lend themselves to structural analysis should be noted and appropriate exercises designed.

There are limitations to the use of structural analysis. When a word is broken into its prefix, root, and suffix, and Greek or Latin meanings are ascribed, the result

---

[4]Deighton, pp. 24-32.

will be a literal translation which may be quite different from the current meaning of the word. For example, photograph = photo + graph = light writing. While this analysis does hint at the process of photography, it is *only* a hint and might be confusing if one were trying to figure out the meaning of a totally unknown word.

Another problem with structural analysis is that many of the prefixes have more than one, often unrelated, meaning. For example, *in-* means *not* in words like *indirect;* it means *into* in words like *incision.*

A third problem with structural analysis is that the initial letters in some words look like prefixes when they aren't, as in the word "equipage". Equi- does not mean *equal* in this case, nor in the word "equine."

Despite these difficulties, knowledge of word parts can be a useful method of figuring out word meanings. This skill, like that of using context clues, involves a problem-solving approach to word study which will continue to be useful to students long after they have left school and word lists far behind.

The following sample exercises and a discussion activity represent different designs with essentially the same approach to teaching word parts. The examples are from mathematics, science, and English.

Sample Exercise: Structural Analysis
Mathematics

The meanings of many mathematical terms can be figured out by looking at the parts of the words, figuring out the meaning of each part, and combining these to give the literal meaning of the word. Look over the list of prefixes, roots, and suffixes below. Then give the meaning of the words.

PREFIXES

semi- = half	octa- = eight	
equi- = equal	rect- = right	
poly- = many	peri- = around	
bi- = two		
tri- = three		
tetra- = three		
quad- = four		
penta- = five		
hexa- = six		
hepta- = seven		

ROOTS

angle
lateral = side
circle
meter = measure

SUFFIXES

-gon = figure having angles
-nomial = names or terms

1. semi- + circle = *semicircle* which means = _____
2. equi- + lateral = *equilateral* which means = _____
3. poly- + gon = *polygon* which means = _____
4. tri- + angle = *triangle* which means = _____
5. quad- + angle = *quadrangle* which means = _____
6. rect- + angle = *rectangle* which means = _____
7. penta- + gon = *pentagon* which means = _____
8. peri- + meter = *perimeter* which means = _____
9. bi- + nomial = *binomial* which means = _____
10. poly- + nomial = *polynomial* which means = _____

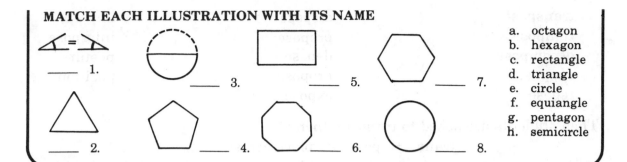

MATCH EACH ILLUSTRATION WITH ITS NAME

_____ 1.

_____ 2.

_____ 3.

_____ 4.

_____ 5.

_____ 6.

_____ 7.

_____ 8.

a. octagon
b. hexagon
c. rectangle
d. triangle
e. circle
f. equiangle
g. pentagon
h. semicircle

Sample Exercise: Structural Analysis
Science or Mathematics

Many people are trying to get the metric system of weights and measurements to be used by everyone in the world. It is not hard to learn the words in the metric system because they are based on our decimal system (that is, based on 10's). The metric system uses eight prefixes to coin very descriptive words.

PREFIXES
micro- = 0.000001 (one millionth)
milli- = 0.001 (one thousandth)
centi- = 0.01 (one hundredth)
deci- = 0.1 (one tenth)
deka- = 10
hecto- = 100
kilo- = 1,000
mega- = 1,000,000

ROOTS
meter = for unit of length
liter = for unit of capacity
gram = for unit of weight
ton = for unit of weight

1. How many liters are in a centiliter? _____
2. How many tons are in a megaton? _____
3. 10 grams = _____ milligrams
4. 1 meter = _____ decimeters
5. 1 kilogram = _____ grams

MAKE UP FIVE OTHER MEASURES AND GIVE THEIR EQUIVALENTS

1. _____
2. _____
3. _____
4. _____
5. _____

Not all exercises need be written. Much vocabulary instruction will occur during the discussion of the reading. Often, through the discussion of one new word, students can be led to *organize* knowledge they already have. For example, suppose the term *appositive* is central to a discussion in a grammar class. Writing the term on the board, the teacher can ask if anyone sees a smaller, familiar word within the new word, e.g. *positive*. Is there a smaller root word even within that word? *pose*. What does *pose* mean? "to place or put". What are some other words that have *pose* as a root or base? List them as students think of them:

transpose	dispose	impose
compose	propose	interpose
decompose	depose	posture
suppose	propose	position
repose	expose	

Then students are asked to translate them:

trans	+	pose	=	place across
com	+	pose	=	place or put together
ex	+	pose	=	put out

Next students are asked to think of forms of these words: *deposit, preposition, proposition, disposal, imposter, repository, etc.* From this discussion, the influence of prefixes (which change meaning) and that of suffixes (which change part of speech) can be seen. Then to get back to the "new" word —*appositive* which means "place next to." From this brief discussion, not only will a "new" word have been taught, but perhaps thirty other words that students already know will be organized for them, thirty words that they may have never associated with one another before. By helping them pattern past knowledge, the new knowledge has a place to "stick"—a context. Opportunities for this type of word study present themselves almost daily.

Use of context clues and structural analysis have been suggested as ways to elicit meaning from unfamiliar words. Another type of vocabulary exercise to be considered is categorizing. Such exercises are best done after students are familiar with the terms to be used since the problem will be one of pointing out relationships among terms. The following categorizing activity was developed for technical literary terms. Note that when an instructor teaches vocabulary, he is directly teaching concepts as well:

Sample Exercise: Categorizing
English Literature

Directions: Carefully read the terms in the following three columns. You will notice category headings below. Place the terms under the headings to which they belong. Some terms may not belong to any category.

iamb	simile	anapest
consonance	naturalism	prosody
allusion	assonance	personification
classicism	pathos	realism
dramatic monologue	trochee	quatrain
alliteration	romanticism	epic
metaphor	farce	tragedy
dactyl	elegy	paradox
comedy	melodrama	sonnet

58

POETIC FEET	SOUND DEVICES	FIGURES OF SPEECH
LITERARY PERIODS	TYPES OF POEMS	TYPES OF PLAYS

All content areas have technical terms to be treated in this manner. A geography teacher, for example, could use this type of exercise to help students put place names with continents. In a history class, events could be matched with the eras in which they occurred.

Another form of vocabulary exercise based on familiar words and one that students tend to enjoy is the word puzzle: scrambled letters to be rearranged with the definition given as the clue, crossword puzzles, anagrams, hidden words, or simple acrostics like the following:

Sample Exercise: Word Puzzle
Social Studies

Directions: Read the definitions at the bottom of the sheet. Fill in the words that match the descriptions in the corresponding spaces.

1. ___ ___ ___ G ___
2. ___ E ___ ___
3. ___ ___ ___ ___ O ___
4. ___ ___ ___ G ___ ___ ___ ___
5. ___ ___ ___ R ___
6. ___ ___ ___ ___ A
7. ___ ___ ___ P ___ ___
8. ___ ___ ___ ___ ___ H ___ ___ ___ ___ ___
9. ___ ___ ___ Y ___ ___ ___

1. The forest of needle-leaved trees in the Soviet Union.
2. A flat-topped mountain or hill usually bordered on one side by a steep cliff.
3. Third largest metropolitan area in the world.
4. Distance in degrees east or west of the Prime Meridian.
5. A long arm of the sea between highlands.
6. A forest of mixed broad-leaved trees in the American basin.
7. Grassy plains of South America.
8. Practice of taking livestock into the highlands during the summer and returning them to lower areas in winter.
9. The world's largest metropolitan area.

Analogies provide another excellent vocabulary activity since they require students to perceive relationships between terms. This is not only good practice for context work, but also for perception of organizational patterns of longer structures. Here are some examples from music:

Sample Exercise: Analogies
Music

Directions: Find the missing terms. Pose the question to yourself like this: "Cello is to string as flute is to what? What is the *relationship* of cello to string? Flute must stand in a similar relationship to something else . . ."

1. cello   : flute
    string   ?

2. largo   : pianissimo
    prestissimo   ?

3. dolce   : animato
    sweetly   ?

4. 4/4   : 2/2
    C   ?

Each teacher should spend time when preparing reading assignments to identify general, technical and special words which could cause reading difficulties. The kind of exercises to be developed (context, structural analysis, categorizing, puzzles, etc.) will depend on the kinds of words and how they are used in the textbook.

KEY TO TEXTBOOKS—Vocabulary

Background/Procedures	Diagnosis	Types of Vocabulary
Burmeister, 126-143; 163-180 Dechant, 205-208 Estes, 185-198 Forgan, 140-151 Hafner, 95-108 Herber, 129-142; 159-172 Karlin, 135-137 Olson, 39 Thomas, 11-24; 63-100 Robinson, 87-88 Roe, 114-135 Shepherd, 41-55 Smith, 119-120; 185-89; 205-216	Estes, 95-103 Thomas, 15-17 Olson, 76-80	Aukerman, 76-78 Dilner, 19-22 Forgan, 152-166 Olson, 73-75 Robinson, 88-89 Roe, 82-86 Smith, 199-201

Context Clues	Structural Analysis	Phonic Analysis	Dictionary Skills
Aukerman, 79 Dechant, 208-214 Dilner, 24-25 Hafner, 110-111 Herber, 143-145 Karlin, 167-173 Olson, 80-82 Thomas, 24-38 Robinson, 90-106 Roe, 87-91 Shepherd, 56-57 Smith, 189-194	Aukerman, 79-80 Burmeister, 143-160; 365-388 Dechant, 215-228 Garland, 109-133 Herber, 145-46 Karlin, 151-157; 173-181 Olson, 82-83 Thomas, 39-55 Roe, 91-101 Shepherd, 66-80 Smith, 194-199; 216-228	Burmeister, 180-187 Dechant, 138-201 Dilner, 25-26 Forgan, 253-291 Garland, 71-108 Hafner, 486-493 Karlin, 140-151 Olson, 83-86 Roe, 101-106 Shepherd, 57-60	Dechant, 232-237 Dilner, 28 Hafner, 109-110 Herber, 146-147 Karlin, 157-161 Olson, 85-87 Thomas, 58-62 Robinson, 89-90, 110 Roe, 106-109 Shepherd, 80-83 Smith, 204-205

See Also:

Deighton, Lee C. *Vocabulary Development in the Classroom.* New York: Teachers College Press, 1965.

Simmons, John S. "Word Study Skills," *Developing Study Skills in Secondary Schools. Reading Perspectives No. 4.* Ed. Harold L. Herber. Newark, Del.: International Reading Association, 1965. 13-31.

ACTIVITY

Using a textbook of your choice, find examples of general, technical and special vocabulary words. Prepare at least 3 different types of exercises. Include examples of the following types: context clues, word (structural) analysis, and word puzzles.

Exercise 4:
VOCABULARY

Context Clues

Structural Analysis

Name _____

Word Puzzle

6

IMPROVING COMPREHENSION

RATIONALE

Understanding what you read while you are reading it—that's comprehension. Though it sounds simple, it is a complex process. Reading is the process of translating symbols into ideas. According to Dechant, it involves the following abilities: to associate experiences and meaning with graphic symbols; to react to visual, auditory, kinesthetic, taste, and smell images suggested by words; to interpret verbal denotations and connotations; to understand words in context and to select the meaning that fits the context; to give meanings to units of increasing size—the phrase, clause, sentence, paragraph, whole selections; to detect and understand the main idea; to recognize significant details; to perceive the organization; to answer questions about a printed page; to follow directions; to perceive relationships—part-whole, cause-effect, general-specific, comparison-contrast, place, size, time, and sequence; to interpret figurative expressions; to make inferences and draw conclusions; to supply implied details; to evaluate what is read; to recognize and understand the writer's purpose; to determine whether the text affirms, denies, or fails to express an opinion or fact or condition; to retain ideas; to apply ideas and integrate them with one's past experience. . . .and so on.

There are, however, various levels of comprehension. Harold L. Herber identifies three levels—literal, interpretive, and applied, each building on the previous one. He describes them in this way:

Literal level. . .produces knowledge of what the author said. . . .It is quite possible for students to identify what an author said, and even memorize and repeat it in class, without understanding what the author meant by his statement.

67

Interpretive level is applied to what the author said in order to derive meaning from his statement. The reader looks for relationships among the statements within the material he has read. From these intrinsic relationships he derives various meanings. . . .

Applied level. . .takes the product of the literal, what the author has said, and the interpretive, what the author meant by what he said, and applies it in some pragmatic or theoretical exercise.[1]

Most reading assignments in the content areas require students to use many skills and processes at various levels. It is for this reason that in doing a content analysis the teacher should consider the skills needed to "comprehend" the material so that reading guides can be prepared to help students develop the skills they need in order to "get" the content. The length, complexity and type of comprehension exercises will vary according to students' abilities and content requirements.

For younger students, or for those who have difficulty in finding the main idea and significant details on an Informal Reading Inventory (see Chapter 8), teachers may wish to design exercises based on phrases, sentences, and paragraphs of different sorts.

PHRASE MEANING

A phrase is more than the sum of the individual words it contains. Words may take on special meanings when they are combined in phrases. For example, when the word *key* is combined with the word *signature* to form the phrase *key signature*, the meaning of the phrase is quite different from the combined denotations of the individual words. The phrases, *fellow traveller, loan shark* and *swan song* certainly mean something quite different than the denoted meanings of the individual words. There are many such specialized phrases in every subject-matter field.

In designing exercises on phrase meaning, examples and explanations such as the ones above are given in the directions section. Students are asked to write the denoted meaning(s) of each word in the phrase, followed by the specialized meaning of the phrase. This points out the difference between the denoted meanings of the individual words and that of the phrase.

---

[1]Harold L. Herber, *Teaching Reading in Content Areas* (Englewood Cliffs, N.J.: Prentice-Hall, Inc., 1970), pp. 62-63.

Sample Exercise: Phrase Meaning
Home Economics

Directions: Many phrases occur in home economics which have special meanings. The words may look familiar to you, yet the meaning of the phrase may still not be clear. Study the example that is done for you below. You will see that the individual words have been defined as they are ordinarily used. Then, the phrase has been given its special meaning. You may use the dictionary or the glossary of your text to do this exercise.

     dotted   spotted

     Swiss   resident of Switzerland

  dotted Swiss   a crisp, cotton fabric embellished
               with woven, flocked, or embroidered dots.

     hard _____

     water _____

  hard water _____

     list _____

     price _____

  list price _____

Another group of phrases that cannot be interpreted literally are expressions such as "chip on his shoulder," "nose out of joint," "foot in his mouth." Again, the meanings of these phrases cannot be ciphered from individuals words. Understanding the use of figurative language in such common phrases as these may help students interpret more difficult passages in literature.

Phrase reading skills of a different nature are most important in reading mathematics. First, there are many common phrases often used in mathematics textbooks that are explanatory in nature; however, many students don't understand what they mean; hence, they don't understand the explanation. The following exercise is designed to help students understand the meanings of such phrases:

Sample Exercise: Phrase Meaning
Mathematics

Here are some words and phrases (groups of words) that may give you trouble in reading mathematics. This exercise will explain how mathematics teachers use the word or phrase and will give you a chance to check your understanding of them.

1. *Express as. . .*"Express as. . ." is used at the beginning of many problems. It means to *write* the answer. (Or *tell,* if the teacher is talking to you.) For example, "Express as a decimal: ¾." This means to *write* ¾ as a decimal. The answer would be .75.

    What does this mean? "Express .25 as a fraction."
    You answer: It means that I should _____ .25 as a fraction.

2. *We will assume that. . .*"We will assume that. . ."is often used when the author wants you to accept something he is going to say as fact. This happens when the author is more interested in what he is going to say next, so he wants you to accept the first piece of information. For example, "We will assume that space people use place value units as we do." The author does not care if these space people are real, he only wants to use this story about space people as an example for you. You are asked to believe this part and to go on from there.

    What does this mean? "We will assume that you are all Romans. How would you write the symbol that shows you mean five objects?

    You answer: It means I would _____ I am a Roman and answer the question as if I really am a Roman.

3. *Consider. . .*"Consider. . ." is a word mathematics teachers often use in place of "Think about this," "Look at this," and "Study this." The author is just trying to get your attention.

    What does this mean? "Consider the number 5235."
    You answer: It means to _____ the number 5235.

4. *Show how. . .is suggested by. . .* You will often see these two phrases together in a sentence. For example, "Show how addition is suggested by XXX." The author wants you to show by writing or telling what it is about the numerals that makes you *think* of addition. When something *suggests* something else, it means it gives you the *idea.*

    What does this mean? "Show how subtraction is suggested by IX."

    You answer: The Roman symbol IX means 9, but it gives the _____ of subtraction because the I means one and the X means ten, so the I in front of X means subtract 1 from 10 to get 9.

5. *Simplify. . .simplest form.* Many times teachers or authors ask you to simplify a number or to give an answer in simplest form. Simplify means to *reduce* the numbers to the most basic elements. For example, "Simplify and multiply 2/4 x 5/25." This means that you should reduce the fractions first:

    $$2/4 = 1/2 \quad 5/25 = 1/5$$

    Then multiply: 1/2 x 1/5 = 1/10. Or, you may have been asked: "Multiply the following. Give answers in simplest form." Using the same problem, you mutiply first, then reduce the answer: 2/4 x 5/25 = 10/100 = 1/10

    What does this mean? "Simplify and add: 8/48 + 3/6 =

    You answer: It means to _____ each fraction to the lowest numbers and then add.

6. *Solve. . .*"Solve" means *to do the operation* that the problem asks you to so. For example, "Solve the following: 3a x 2b." This means to look at the sign (x) and do what that sign tells you. In this case, it means to multiply the two numbers to find the answer.

    What does this mean? "Solve the following: 3c – 2c = _____."

    You answer: I am to _____ the two numbers to find the _____.

7. *Translate. . .*"Translate" is used in mathematics the same way it is used in foreign language. In foreign language, you are asked to translate an English sentence to a Spanish sentence, for example. In mathematics, it means to write an English sentence or phrase in *math language.* For example, "Translate two times a number divided by five" means to *write* this using numbers, letters, and signs: 2y ÷ 5 or 2y/5.

    What does this mean? "Translate the phrase, "six times a number."

You answer: I am to _____ these words in math language by using letters, numbers, and/or signs. The answer is _____.

8. *Prove*. . . When mathematics teachers want you to prove something, they want you *to give examples* to show that a statement is true. For example, "Prove that the commutative property of addition works for this set of numbers: 3 + 4 =." This means that you must show by example that the statement is true: 3 + 4 = 7 and 4 + 3 = 7.

What does this mean? "Prove that the commutative property of multiplication works with this set of numbers: 3 x 4 = 12."

You answer: _____ and _____.

Another critical phrase reading skill in mathematics is needed in setting up mathematical word problems. Students must be able to translate English phrases into mathematical phrases. The following example illustrates how complex this task can be:

Sample Exercise: Phrase Meaning
Mathematics

The Problem: There are three consecutive integers where the sum of the first and third is 11 more than the second integer. Find the integers.

Step 1:   Reading the first phrase, "There are three consecutive integers," the student begins to translate by assuming x to be the first integer. The word *consecutive* should imply that $x + 1$ would follow as the second and $x + 2$ as the third.

Step 2:   Reading the second phrase, "where the sum of the first and third," the student should translate that he adds the first integer *(x)* to the third (x + 2).

Step 3:   The next word, "is", may be translated (=) or "the same as."

Step 4:   Reading the final phrase, "11 more than the second integer," the student translates that 11 is added to the second integer: *11 + (x + 1)*.

Step 5:   Since in Step 3 the student learns that Steps 2 and 4 indicate an equation, the problem may be set up as follows:

x + (x + 2)	=	11 + (x + 11)
Step 2	Step 3	Step 4

Step 6:   Having used reading skills to translate the problem from an English sentence to a mathematic sentence, mathematics skills may be used to solve for the three numbers.[2]

Notice that in this one-sentence problem, the student had to know special and technical vocabulary words *(consecutive, integer, sum, is)* in order translate the phrases. The translation required five steps before math skills could be used to perform the operations. For many students, the greatest difficulty in mathematics is finding or "dis-covering" the problem. The exercise below is intended to help

_____

[2]Developed by Molly Crews.

71

develop phrase reading skills. The arrows are important because they help students to see how symbols are often flip-flopped when translating from English to math.

Sample Exercise: Phrase Meaning
Mathematics

Many problems in math can be solved if you can translate them from English sentences or phrases into mathematical sentences or phrases. Below are several English phrases that have been translated for you. Study them. Then see if you can do the matching exercise which follows.

ENGLISH PHRASE   MATHEMATICAL PHRASE

A number | increased by six   a | + 6

Six times | a number   6 x | n   (or, 6n)

Four less than | a number   y | - 4

A number | divided by five   x | ÷ 5 or $\frac{x}{5}$

Four less than | thirty times a number   30 b | - 4

Matching

_____ 1. the sum of x and ten   a. y - 6

_____ 2. five times a number   b. b + 5

_____ 3. a number increased by five   c. 6 - c

_____ 4. a number divided by two   d. x + 10

_____ 5. four less than five times a number e. $\frac{s}{2}$

_____ 6. six minus a number   f. 5t

_____ 7. a number decreased by seven   g. 2n + 5

_____ 8. the product of nine and n   h. z - 7

_____ 9. five greater than two times a number   i. 5p - 4

_____ 10. the difference between six and a number   j. 9n

SENTENCE MEANING

A great deal of information can be compressed into a relatively short sentence as was demonstrated in the mathematics problem on page 71. This is an example of a heavy concept load. (Concept load was discussed earlier in the chapter on readability.) If reading is the process of translating symbols into ideas and *understanding* them, it is a worthy accomplishment to achieve even the *literal* level of comprehension in reading intricate sentences which have been written in complicated terms in order to explain difficult concepts. The following sentence from a high school chemistry book illustrates the point because a number of concepts are stated and implied in it. Several questions have been based on this one sentence.

Sample Exercise: Sentence Meaning
Chemistry

When you review the oxidation-reduction properties of the Row 3 elements, you do see a rather smooth trend in behavior from the strong reducing agent sodium, through the elements like phosphorus and sulfur which are neither strong reducing agents nor strong oxidizing agents, and finally to the strong oxidizing agent chlorine, where the reducing tendency is very low.[3]

1. What two properties are you asked to review?
2. Define each property.
3. Where can all the elements listed in the sentence be found on the periodic chart?
4. How are phosphorus and sulfur related in terms of the properties you are asked to review?
5. Looking at the periodic chart, what other element would you expect to act in a manner similar to P and S?
6. Is the reducing tendency stronger on the left of the periodic chart than on the right?
7. Would Mg be a strong oxidizing agent? Explain your answer in terms of its position on the chart.
8. Though argon is inert chemically, how is it related to chlorine in terms of physical properties?
9. Does there seem to be a relationship between an element's physical properties and its oxidation-reduction properties? If so, state the relationship.
10. The following concepts are either stated or implied in the above sentence. Fill in the blanks to complete each statement:
   a. The elements discussed in the reading occur in Row _____ of the periodic chart.
   b. Elements on the left of the periodic chart are strong _____ agents.
   c. If you disregard the inert gases, elements on the right of the periodic chart are strong _____ agents.
   d. Elements in the middle of Row 3 show both _____ and _____ properties, but they are not strong agents.

The sentence and relatively brief exercise above could be the foundation of one or more class discussions on why Row 3 elements act as they do in terms of their oxidation-reduction properties and their related physical properties. In fact, the chapter from which the sentence is taken describes these reasons, but the explanations are long and complicated and rely heavily on models, diagrams, and formulas. The basic concept (that as you move from left to right, Row 3 elements

---

[3]Albert Cotton and Lawrence D. Lynch, *Chemistry: An Investigative Approach* (Boston: Houghton Mifflin Company, 1968), p. 483.

continue the trend away from strong reducing properties) can be discovered by students through judicious teacher questioning once the students have read the above sentence and completed the questions. Reading of the chapter in its entirety could then *follow* the discussion with increased student comprehension. The applied level of comprehension could then be achieved by having students observe some of the physical and chemical properties of third row elements in an experiment or lab demonstration.

Some students may gain more understanding of important concepts by having a teacher guide their reading of a few key sentences than they could acquire from struggling on their own through an entire chapter. The following sample exercise (based on sentences taken from *World Geography,* 4th ed., by John H. Bradley, Ginn and Co., 1971) demonstrates the kinds of questions that can be developed from relatively simple sentences.

Sample Exercise: Sentence Meaning
Social Studies

Directions: Read the sentences and answer the questions which follow.

1. The first and most important fact of human geography is that the world's population, more than three billion people, live on the earth's 197 million square miles of land surface.
   A. What kind of geography is being discussed? _____
   B. How many people live on the earth? _____
   C. What is the average number of people per square mile (approximately)? _____
   D. Is this an important fact? Why do you think so? Or why not?
      _____

2. Some 300 years ago, the great British scientist, Sir Isaac Newton, stated the laws of motion and gravity.
   A. What does "stated" mean? _____
   B. Did Newton state his laws in the 1500's, the 1600's or the 1700's? _____
   C. Where did Newton live? _____
   D. What kind of laws are being discussed? What were they about? _____
      _____

3. Within the Arctic Circle, in the Land of the Midnight Sun, the summer sun is above the horizon throughout all twenty-four hours.
   A. What is "the horizon?" _____
   B. What part of the earth is being discussed? _____
   C. How many hours a day can you see the sun? _____
   D. What season of the year is it when this happens? _____
   E. Why is the Arctic specially called "The Land of the Midnight Sun?" _____
   F. .What might happen in the winter? _____ _____

4. Because different types of vegetation are the result of different types of climates, the general world pattern of vegetation belts corresponds to the general world pattern of climate belts.
   A. What is the cause of different types of vegetation? _____
   B. What two "belts" are being discussed? _____

C. What is meant by "belts?" _____

D. What does "correspond" mean? _____

E. How are the patterns of vegetation related to the patterns of climate? _____

5. Rising warm air cools as it rises, contracts, grows heavier, and then sinks to the earth's surface.

    (Number the steps in the order that describes what happens to rising warm air.)

    _____ grows heavier

    _____ rises and cools

    _____ contracts

    _____ sinks to earth

6. Southern Chile is mountainous, like the Pacific Northwest, but it is windier, wetter, and colder.

    A. What country is under discussion here? _____

    B. What specific part of the country is being described? _____

    C. How is it like the Pacific Northwest? _____

    D. How is it different? _____

7. As one travels south along the west coast of the United States to between 30° and 40° latitude, the temperature becomes milder, but the moisture decreases.

    A. What is "latitude?" _____

    _____

    B. What is the *range* of latitude given? _____

    C. What geographic area is being discussed? _____

    _____

    D. What increases? _____

    E. What decreases? _____

8. Though not all the visitors and not any of the neighbors agree, the residents of Southern California are pretty generally certain that the mediterranean climate, as expressed in North America, is the finest climate on earth.

    A. What kind of climate is being discussed? _____

    B. What does the word "mediterranean" mean? _____

    C. Where can this type of climate be found in North America? _____

    D. Who thinks this is the finest climate on earth? _____

    _____

    E. Who disagrees? _____

9. For centuries before the first white men came into the valley of the Rio Grande in southern New Mexico, the Pueblo Indians had practiced the art of irrigation there.

    A. What kind of Indians are discussed here? _____

    B. Where did these Indians live? _____

    C. What kind of body of water is indicated by "the valley of the Rio Grande?" _____

    D. What "art" have these Indians practiced? _____

    E. How long have they done it? _____

    F. What is it? What happens? _____

    G. Why did they do it? _____

    H. How do you suppose they did it? _____

10. For centuries, the stormy lands of the wet, middle latitudes have been described as "temperate," which means "free from extremes."
   A. What does "temperate" mean? _____
   B. In what latitudes are the lands being discussed? _____
   _____
   C. Does it rain a lot here? _____
   D. How long have these lands been called temperate? _____
   E. What kind of "extremes" are these lands free from? _____
   F. What countries do you suppose are in this area? _____
   _____

The full meaning of a sentence depends upon punctuation; word order; grammatical inflections which signal tense, number, and possession; and on such key words as *because* and *nevertheless*. If a reader cannot understand and interpret these language patterns in sentences, he will have difficulty with paragraphs and longer selections.

The next exercise concentrates on reading the *punctuation* of the sentence in order to call students' attention to the fact that punctuation does have meaning and is often used in place of words. An exercise such as this does not necessarily have to be written. It can be incorporated into class discussions. The important thing is that the teacher become aware of the many "teachable moments" created by the printed text itself.

Sample Exercise: Meaning from Punctuation
Home Economics

1. All-purpose flour is usually enriched by adding iron and B vitamins—thiamine (B_1), niacin, and riboflavin (B_2).
   A. What does the dash (—) tell you? _____
   B. Why are B_1 and B_2 set off in parentheses? _____
2. Toasted rolls, page 80, and croutons (kroo-tons') are good to serve with soup.
   A. Why is *page 80* set off in commas? Why is it in this sentence at all?
   _____
   B. What information is found within the parentheses? _____
3. Butter, shortening, and margarine are fats that make breads, cakes, and pastries tender, that is, they "shorten" baked flour mixtures.
   A. What do the commas after the words *butter* and *shortening* indicate?
   _____
   B. What do the commas before and after *that is* indicate to you?
   _____
   C. Why is the word *shorten* placed in quotation marks?
   _____
4. Only three of the nutrients—carbohydrates, fats, and proteins—supply calories.
   A. Why are the dashes there? _____

    B.   What words do the dashes replace? _____

5.   Sweet snacks and so-called "soft" drinks are rich in calories from sugar though they have few, if any, other food values.
    A.   Why is *soft* put into quotation marks? _____

    B.   Why is *if any* set off in commas? What purpose does this phrase serve?

    _____

6.   The dark green, leafy vegetables (spinach and turnip greens, for example) are notable for the amount of vitamins and minerals they contain.
    A.   What purpose is served by the parentheses that enclose *spinach and turnip greens?*

    _____

    B.   Why is *for example* set off in commas? _____

7.   "Alas," as Aldous Huxley said, ". . . in the matter of diet, most people will find it . . . mortifying to refrain from eating all the things which the experts in nutrition condemn as unwholesome."
    A.   Why are quotation marks used in this sentence? _____

    B.   What do the three dots (. . .) mean? _____

PARAGRAPH MEANING
Reading for Main Ideas and Details

The most basic skill in reading paragraphs is to be able to identify the main idea. This skill is founded upon accurate comprehension of word, phrase, and sentence. Without the ability to find main ideas, students cannot hope to identify theme, figure out the author's meaning, or recall information. Implied meanings will go unnoticed.

Work on paragraph comprehension might begin with well-organized paragraphs which have the main idea explicitly stated at the beginning. News articles are good examples. Short articles, with headlines cut off, may be matched by students with the headlines. Or, they might be asked to write their own headlines.

Extend the skill of finding main ideas to paragraphs in which the central idea is found in the middle or at the end. When students have demonstrated competence in picking out the main idea, help them to elaborate it with significant details. One way to help them do this is with a technique which has been called "mapping." Design exercises based on a paragraph so that, when the exercise is completed, the result will be a diagram of the paragraph. This idea is similar to the structured overview discussed in Chapter 6, in that it produces a visual representation of the relationship among the ideas contained in a selection. M. Buckley Hanf describes mapping this way:

A map is a graphic representation of the intellectual territory travelled or to be travelled via reading. It is a verbal picture of ideas which are organized and symbolized by the reader. Map making, an exercise in critical thinking, demands the student's insightful judgments and discriminate decisions about the material. First, the reader decides the map's starting point by locating the primary thesis or main idea. Next, he determines the secondary categories or principal parts. After labeling these parts, the reader connects them with the main idea. He now has a picture of the basic structure of the material. The next and last step is adding supporting details. One cannot make a map without being keenly involved in critical thinking.[4]

The following exercise demonstrates a variation of the use of maps.

Sample Exercise: Main Idea and Supporting Details
Art—Ceramics

Directions: Using the paragraph below, find the main idea. Write this in as the title. The supporting ideas are given on the diagram. Fill in additional details about each supporting idea.

A teapot is a functional item. It may be beautiful to look at, but if it does not serve its purposes well, it will be a failure as a ceramic item. Before throwing begins, the potter must carefully consider the design of each part in terms of its function. The bottom should sit securely. The handle should be well balanced, yet designed so that it will not become too hot. The spout should pour properly requiring the strainer to be large enough and low enough to prevent clogging with tea leaves. The lid should be flanged so that it will not fall out when serving the tea.

Spout _____

Lid _____

Title:

Handle _____

Strainer _____

Bottom _____

[4]M. Buckley Hanf, "Mapping: A Technique for Translating Reading into Thinking." *Journal of Reading,* 14 (Jan. 1971), p. 225.

Once students have shown the ability to find the important features of a paragraph and relate them to each other, help them to extend their skill still further by giving them exercises based on paragraphs in which the main idea has been implied. They may be led through the process of determining the main idea and then be asked to state it in their own words. The following sample exercises provide examples.

Sample Exercise: Main Idea of a Paragraph—Implied
Social Studies

Directions: Read the paragraph below and then fill in the diagram based on the information you read. The object is to find the main idea of the selection. Since the main idea is not directly stated, you will need to reason it out.

In the short span of three years, world industrial production had dropped to one-third of what it had been in 1930. More and more people lost their jobs. By 1933, more than 13 million people were out of work in the United States, 3 million in Great Britain and 6 million in Germany. France was the only leading industrial nation that did not suffer unemployment in critical proportions. This was attributed to France's relative scarcity of labor, consistency of population, and balance of economy.

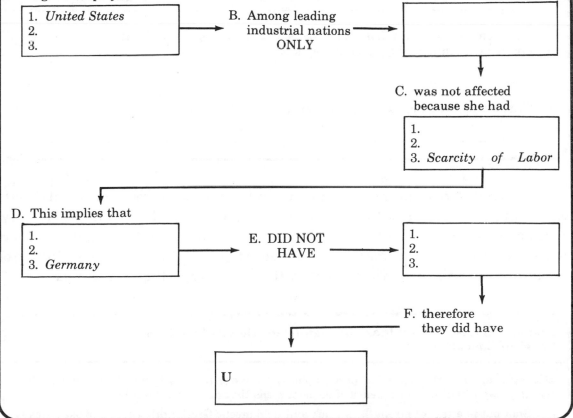

A. Industrial nations with
   high unemployment were

   1. *United States*
   2.
   3.

B. Among leading
   industrial nations
   ONLY

C. was not affected
   because she had

   1.
   2.
   3. *Scarcity of Labor*

D. This implies that

   1.
   2.
   3. *Germany*

E. DID NOT
   HAVE

   1.
   2.
   3.

F. therefore
   they did have

U

Sometimes main ideas are not directly stated in a paragraph. Read the paragraph below and do the exercise to help you write a topic sentence.

It is exciting to see new and unusual places. But I couldn't see very much if I stayed close to home all the time. I also find that traveling helps me with my school-work. It often introduces me to ideas, people, and places that I later study in my textbooks. I find that travel makes me more interesting as a person. I have more things to talk about when with other people, and they seem more interested in what I have to say. But most important, I guess, is that traveling allows me to get away from the boring routine of everyday living. It lets me operate on a different time schedule than I'm used to and lets me do more of what I enjoy doing.

A. Find nine details that the writer of this paragraph tells you about his subject and list them below.

1. _____   6. _____

2. _____   7. _____

3. _____   8. _____

4. _____   9. _____

5. _____

B. Based on the ideas you listed, what would you say is the general topic discussed in this paragraph?

_____

C. Based on the ideas you listed and the general topic, do you think that the writer feels favorably or unfavorably about his subject?

_____

D. Write a topic sentence expressing the main idea of this paragraph.

_____

The next exercise presents yet another way to show the relationship of details to a main idea. It also asks the student to distinguish unrelated details. Frequently, significant details will fall into a logical pattern. Attention to the pattern (time, steps of a procedure, etc.) may help the reader to recall details to mind. Matters of paragraph organization will be dealt with more fully in the next section.

Directions: Read the following paragraphs and answer the questions which follow. While reading, pay attention to sequence of ideas or steps that are being described.

Shot put is a test of strength in track and field meets. Greek athletes used to use a heavy stone. Today athletes use iron balls of various weights. Beginners use 8 pound balls; seniors use 16 pound balls.

To shot put, you stand at the back of a circle which is seven feet in diameter. The shot is balanced on your fingers. Then you glide or hop until your leading foot hits the wooden stop board at the front of the circle. You than propel the shot, getting your whole body force behind the shot. As you do so, the momentum will force you to turn your body so that the position of your feet will be reversed, and your weight shifts to your other foot. It is important to throw your arm out in a long follow-through. The most effective angle to send the shot in the air is 40°.[5]

Next to following sentences, write these symbols to indicate

| ⊕ main idea | ⊛ too broad |
| ⚹◯ important detail | ⚹ ◯ totally unrelated to paragraph |

_____ It is important to have a good follow-through to get distance in putting the shot.

_____ To put a shot involves a series of moves.

_____ The Olympics is an important athletic event.

_____ High jumping is a track and field event.

On the lines below, list in order the steps you go through to put a shot.

1. _____

2. _____

3. _____

4. _____

5. _____

6. _____

Reading for Organization

Most information in textbooks is presented in basic patterns which stress a relationship among the ideas. The basic patterns are: time sequence; comparison/contrast; cause/effect; simple listing; step-by-step procedures; and categorization. Since a good writer wants to be understood, he will use signal words to let the reader know what pattern he is using. The emphasis in teaching students to observe paragraph organization, then, is on noting the key words which indicate the patterns being used and seeing relationships among the ideas being presented. Words like *first, next, third,* and *finally* are clues that the author is listing details or steps in a procedure. *By contrast, on the other hand, however, yet* are signals of comparison/contrast statements. Cues to chronological organization are such words as *initially, then, soon, later, after that, at last.* Directing students' attention to signal words within paragraphs will greatly aid them in reading longer selections since whole chapters are often patterned in this way.

The various paragraph formats lend themselves to different kinds of exercises. The following exercise is based upon a paragraph by Isocrates which lists the qualities of an educated man. He begins by asking a question to establish the topic.

---

[5] *World Book Encyclopedia,* 1973 ed., s.v. "Shot-put," by Fred Russell.

Then he answers the question in a 169-word sentence which is well developed and nicely divided by means of signal words. Finally, he gives a summary statement which specifies what he means by "educated".

Sample Exercise: Paragraph Organization
Literature

Directions: In the following paragraph, Isocrates' answer to the question, "What is an educated man?" is a long one. Note, however, that he divides his description into four sections. Read the selection, then do the exercise.

Whom, then, do I call educated, since I exclude the arts and sciences and specialties? First, those who manage well the circumstances which they encounter day by day, and who possess a judgment which is accurate in meeting occasions as they arise and rarely miss the expedient course of action; next, those who are decent and honourable in their intercourse with all with whom they associate, tolerating easily and good-naturedly what is unpleasant or offensive in others and being themselves as agreeable and reasonable to their associates as it is possible to be; furthermore, those who hold their pleasures always under control and are not unduly overcome by their misfortunes, bearing up under them bravely and in a manner worthy of our common nature; finally, and most important of all, those who are not spoiled by successes and do not desert their true selves and become arrogant, but hold their ground steadfastly as intelligent men, not rejoicing in the good things which have come to them through chance rather than in those which through their own nature and intelligence are theirs from their birth. Those who have a character which is in accord, not with one of these things, but with all of them—these, I contend, are wise and complete men, possessed of all the virtues.[6]

1. Underline those words which indicate a division in the listing of characteristics of an educated man. (Answer: first, next, furthermore, finally)
2. Write these words below as headings to columns. Under each column, write nouns, verbs, or adjectives that Isocrates uses to describe an educated man:
   Answer:

First	Next	Furthermore	Finally
manages	decent	self-controlled	not spoiled
circumstances	honorable	not overcome by	by success
	tolerant	misfortune	
has accurate	good-natured		not arrogant
judgment	agreeable		
	reasonable		true to self
acts expediently			
			rejoices in
			successes
			gained through
			intelligence,
			hard-work

3. Each of the four divisions could be paragraphs themselves describing how an educated man conducts himself in each of four areas. What would the topic of each paragraph be? That is, what kind of situation would be discussed in each?

---

[6]From *Isocrates, Volume II, Oration V, "Panathenaicus,"* translated by George Norlin (Loeb Classical Library). Reprinted in *Outlooks through Literature,* ed. by Robert C. Pooley, (Chicago: Scott, Foresman and Co., 1964), pp. 406-07.

Answer:
a. meeting the occasion, taking advantage of opportunities
b. relationships with others
c. self-control
d. true relation to self

This kind of exercise could well precede the questions posed in the text itself, questions which do not address themselves to the problems of literal, or even interpretive comprehension—what the author said and what he meant by what he said. An assumption has been made by the editors, either that the students will comprehend concepts and relationships without assistance, or, that the teacher will provide assistance. The four questions posed in the text are all on the applied level. The first asks the student to make a judgment and a comparison between Isocrates' statement and "the modern concept"—a problem that few ninth graders will be anxious to tackle unless they have been well-prepared for it.

Other kinds of exercises may be designed to increase comprehension of paragraphs which involve time order or list steps to be followed in sequence (e.g., recipes, how to execute various techniques in sports, and directions to be followed). These can be presented in "jumbled sequence." Students may be asked to put them back in proper sequence by placing the number "1" next to the statement or step which comes first; the number "2" next to the second step, and so forth.

Sample Exercise: Paragraph Organization—Jumbled Sequence Mathematics

Suppose you want to buy some wall-to-wall carpeting for your bedroom. You have seen advertisements of the carpeting you want. It costs $5.95 a square yard. You have saved $100. Your bedroom measures 10 feet by 18 feet. Do you have enough money to buy the carpeting you want?

To solve this problem, first you must find the floor area of your bedroom. To do this, you multiply the length by the width (10′ x 18′). Your answer will be 180 square feet. Since the carpeting is sold in square *yards*, you must figure out how many square yards are in 180 square feet. To do this, we know that 3 feet equals a yard. A square yard, then, would be 3′ x 3′ or 9 square feet equals one square yard. Your bedroom had 180 square feet. To change it to square yards, you divide 180 by 9 which equals 20 square yards. The next step is to determine how much 20 square yards of carpeting costs at $5.95 per square yard. Multiply 20 x $5.95 which equals $119.00. Do you have enough money? _____.

To solve the problem, we went through a series of steps which are listed below in jumbled order. Rearrange them so they are in the proper sequence. Do this by placing a number in front of each step: 1, 2, 3, 4, and 5.

_____ 3 ft. x 3 ft. = 9 sq. ft. = 1 sq. yd.

_____ 10 ft. x 18 ft. = area of room in sq. ft.

_____ Number of sq. yds. x cost per sq. yd. = cost of carpeting bedroom.

_____ 180 sq. ft. divided by 9 sq. yds. = number of sq. yds. in bedroom.

_____ cost of carpeting minus the money you have.

If a paragraph presents information in a cause and effect pattern, causes can be listed in one column, effects in another. Comparison/contrast lends itself to charting in a similar fashion.

Sample Exercise: Paragraph Organization—Cause and Effect
Psychology/Human Development

Directions: Read the following paragraph paying attention to causes and effects. Then, complete the chart. Note that effects may be both good and bad.

What a person learns and how he learns it will be determined by the kinds of learning opportunities provided in his environment. The wider the variety of people and experiences available to him, the better prepared will the person be for life. A person who grows up among books, who is read to as a child and who is encouraged to read, generally acquires a taste for reading and holds literature in high regard. A person who grows up in a group limited to persons of one race who distrust those of other races, is likely to grow into a prejudiced adult. If the environment is felt to be too limiting, some persons may leave the family and find their own opportunities. Their behavior may later be quite different from that of other family members. Heredity plays a role, too. A person may have the advantage of having inherited great intellectual capacity; nevertheless, it must be developed. The person of less than average intellectual capacity, if developed to the fullest extent, may surpass in achievement the person with a greater capacity who did not, or was not able to make full use of it.[7]

CAUSES	EFFECTS
Environment, wide & varied	Excellent preparation for life

---

[7]Based on information in Susan Irving, *Basic Psychiatric Nursing,* 2nd ed. (Philadelphia: W. B. Saunders Company), p. 41.

Directions: Read the following paragraph. Two kinds of things are being compared and contrasted. After you have read the selection, fill in the chart.

Litmus is a blue powder derived from certain lichens. Litmus changes to red with increasing acidity and to blue with increasing alkalinity. Scientists use paper impregnated with litmus to determine if a compound is an acid or a base. If you put a drop or two of vinegar on blue litmus paper, the blue color would change to pink since vinegar contains a compound called acetic acid. If you did the same thing to pink litmus paper, the paper would stay pink. On the other hand, if you put a couple of drops of household ammonia on pink litmus paper, it would turn blue because household ammonia contains a compound called ammonium hydroxide which is a member of a large group of compounds called bases. Bases turn pink litmus paper blue.

List two classes of compounds	List an example of each kind of compound	Results of blue litmus paper test	Results of pink litmus paper test

What do vinegar and ammonium hydroxide have in common? _____

How are they different? _____

MEANING FROM LONGER SELECTIONS
Chapters and Units

For those students who are moderately successful on the comprehension portion of the Informal Reading Inventory and for more advanced students who seem to have little difficulty in basic comprehension skills, teachers can design reading study guides for longer selections like chapters, units, even entire books. In a study guide, questions should be written on various cognitive levels to stimulate reading at each of the three levels of comprehension—literal, interpretive and applied.

Study guides (Chapter 10) also include exercises which promote critical reading and activities which may help students in integrating what they have read into their lives. You will be asked to prepare a reading study guide as the culminating activity in this workbook. In order to write a study guide, you will find it necessary to use all of the skills and information that you will have acquired in the course of this study. For secondary teachers, the reading study guide might be the principal teaching method employed since it blends reading study skills with content instruction.

The topic is mentioned here since many teachers may feel that it will be difficult to include the comprehension exercises you will be preparing in this section in a lesson having broader scope. Though presently isolated, exercises in vocabulary, comprehension and graphics may be designed as parts of a whole—the study guide—which, in its turn, is based on larger units of instruction.

INFORMATION SOURCES

Textbooks in the field of teaching reading in the content areas generally devote a major portion of the text to the development of vocabulary and comprehension skills. This is entirely logical since the ultimate aim of the subject-matter teacher is to help students understand the fundamental ideas within a discipline. The following texts will provide insight into basic comprehension skills, abundant examples of how to develop these skills from phrase exercises to those involving critical reading, and a wealth of information about special comprehension skill development within the various content areas. It is recommended that some of these sources be carefully read before attempting the activities in this section.

KEY TO TEXTBOOKS—Comprehension

Skills/Levels	Sentence	Main Idea/Details
Burmeister, 192-204; 236-254 Dechant, 244-248 Dilner, 39-42 Estes, 66-68 Garland, 134-149 Hafner, 127-134 Herber, 37-71 Karlin, 165-167 Olson, 124-127 Robinson, 24; 117-121 Shepherd, 86-88 Smith, 33-35; 153-154; 231-234	Dechant, 249-252 Karlin, 181-186 Robinson, 45-46 Roe, 135-140 Shepherd, 104-107 Smith, 157	Aukerman, 65-76 Burmeister, 204-211 Dechant, 252-258 Dilner, 43-46 Hafner, 135-138 Karlin, 209-219 Olson, 39-43 Robinson, 46-48 Roe, 147-150 Shepherd, 91-92 Thomas, 184-189
Organizational Patterns	**Critical Reading**	**Questioning/Guiding**
Burmeister, 211-231 Dechant, 258-262 Dilner, 46-49; 76-78 Hafner, 138-146 Herber, 72-102 Karlin, 186-192 Robinson, 136-156 Roe, 150-155 Shepherd, 93-103	Aukerman, 83-85 Burmeister, 256-294 Dechant, 268-272 Dilner, 49-61 Hafner, 146-157 Herber, 103-120 Karlin, 192-201 Olson, 61-71 Robinson, 126-129; 201-203; 283 284 Shepherd, 107-109	Forgan, 170-204 Garland, 149-191 Herber, 190-200 Olson, 127-128 Robinson, 123-124 Roe, 155-165 Shepherd, 88-90 Smith, 240-249 Thomas, 169-183

Also see:

> Niles, Olive S. "Organization Perceived," *Developing Study Skills in Secondary Schools. Perspectives in Reading No. 4.* Ed. Harold L. Herber. Newark, Del.: International Reading Association, 1965. 57-76.

ACTIVITY

Using the textbook of your choice or other materials within your discipline, complete comprehension exercises for each of the following: phrase meaning, sentence meaning, finding main ideas and significant details of paragraphs, and finding organizational patterns in various types of paragraphs.

Exercise 5:

COMPREHENSION

Phrase Meaning

(Select ten phrases which are specialized phrases in your discipline, *e.g.*, divine right, low relief, brake shoe, free lance, loving cup, or idiomatic expressions. Prepare an exercise based on these phrases.)

Sentence Meaning

(Select five sentences of various types, lengths and complexities. Ask a series of questions based on each sentence.)

Paragraph Meaning: Main Ideas and Details

(Select four paragraphs—one with the main idea stated initially; one in which the main idea is stated at the end; one in which the main idea is within the body of the paragraph; and one in which the main idea is not explicity stated, but implied. Copy each paragraph below. Under each paragraph, write a series of questions to develop students' skill in finding the main idea and significant details.)

(Paragraph Meaning: Main Idea and Details, continued)

Paragraph Meaning: Organizational Patterns

(Select four paragraphs, one each for the following organizational patterns—time order, enumerative order (simple listing), cause/effect, and comparison/contrast. Copy each paragraph below and devise exercises for each pattern which stress perception of the organization as well as comprehension of the relationship of the ideas.)

(Paragraph Meaning: Organizational Patterns, continued)

94

7

INTERPRETING GRAPHICS

RATIONALE

In textbooks, the purpose served by graphics of all kinds is, first of all, to reinforce and clarify concepts contained within the printed portions, and secondly, to make the book appear interesting and attractive.

Primary pupils use very colorful books, profusely illustrated. As they move through the grades, the number of illustrations decreases as the quantity of print increases. By the time they have advanced to reading college texts, illustrations have become fewer and the use of color has diminished as greater reliance is placed upon comprehension of the printed word and as motivation is presumed to come more from within than from without.

Modern textbooks on all levels and in all areas use a far greater variety and profusion of graphic material than were used even a generation ago. Photographs, paintings and cartoons, as well as graphs, charts, diagrams, tables and maps all have a place in today's texts.

Illustrations are helpful insofar as they reinforce and clarify meaning without becoming commonplace and redundant. Colorful is wonderful if the net result is to increase interest and enhance understanding of the concepts presented rather than to promote confusion and distraction.

Though visual presentations have features in common, each kind has its own special way of conveying meaning. This is true even within a particular class of graphic material. By their nature, some may be more suited than others to the presentation of a particular piece of information: a schematic diagram is sure to be of more help in gaining understanding of how an electrical circuit works than the most gorgeous photograph of the winning entry in the science fair. On the other hand, a full color reproduction of Van Gogh's *Sunflowers* will do more to enhance understanding of how an artist may use and apply line and color than any number of diagrams. These are obvious examples, but there is a choice to make, too, in deciding whether to show the federal budget on a bar graph or a pie graph.

Teachers are frequently not aware of how useful a good visual aid can be. An entire lesson may be built around one graph, map, cartoon, photograph. Using graphics and careful questioning techniques, a teacher can help students discover concepts which were, perhaps, too abstract for them in verbal form. However, in order to lead students through an interpretation of graphic materials with ease and confidence, one must be aware of the kinds of graphic materials and their potential usefulness, as well as the reading problems inherent in each.

Content teachers should insure that students are competent in using the visual aids common to the subject matter. If graphics are to be as effective a tool as they can be, both in class and in the student's later life, teachers must lead students to read them critically, analyzing and interpreting, making inferences and drawing conclusions based on the information provided.

PROCESS OF READING GRAPHICS

Graphics supplement narratives, clarify ideas, expand experience, aid in avoiding misunderstanding. They are effective in showing step-by-step procedures, comparing and contrasting, illustrating status and/or relationships of things, demonstrating processes, describing scenes and events. They can provide a visual, concrete pattern of information which is useful in thinking analytically. In fact, intelligent use of graphics can contribute to the development of skill in analytic thinking. Good graphics can be used to promote recognition of particular objects, places, processes, people, and can enable the viewer to name these and note details about them. Appropriate graphics encourage the perception of relationships between and among details. From these relationships, inferences may be drawn and against them, hypotheses may be tested. But, graphics can reflect opinion, bias, and value judgments, too. Criticial thinking skills may be extended in detecting flaws and in appraising the information presented in a graphic. It will be observed, therefore, that many of the skills required in the reading and thinking processes that apply to verbal material are also applicable to the reading and interpretation of graphics.

In order to read graphics, as to read print, one must perceive the symbol, distinguish it from other symbols, and attach meaning to it. If, in reading a map, one perceives "blue" among a number of other colors, one must then ask what it means. Water, perhaps? Or, temperatures 0 to 20 degrees, or places where French is spoken, or where Hinduism is practiced, or where sickle cell anemia is rampant? It depends upon the meaning assigned by the map maker. Map symbols, like words, don't mean much in isolation. Furthermore, knowing that blue represents altitudes between 1000 and 5000 feet won't mean much outside of the context of a particular map.

Maps are used in all content areas at one time or another, and students need to know how to read them. Students generally do read maps with a fair degree of competence, having been taught in elementary school. Teachers in the content areas often feel secure in the knowledge that this skill has been taught. They may think that map reading is simple and that the skill has been mastered. However, there are so many different kinds of maps—street maps, road maps, relief maps, physical maps, historical maps, literary maps, war maps, weather maps, and so on. When one considers the amount of information that can be represented on a map in addition to the variety of kinds, map reading may then be understood as a skill that can be extended and developed to a high level of sophistication. Though a student "learned to read maps" in third or fourth grade, this doesn't necessarily mean he has nothing left to learn about map reading when he is a high school senior.

Beyond the primary grades, one of the most common types of visual representation is the graph. Graphs are especially helpful in showing how numerical data are related. Comparisons among various subsets may be easily made. Periods of time (e.g., years, decades) may be graphed in relation to dollars spent, population may be graphed against land area, percentages of a whole may be shown in relation to each other and to the whole—the relationship is always based upon quantities. There are several kinds of graphs and each has its special uses. These are charted on page 101.

A great deal of literal information can often be collected from a single graph, map, or chart. It is unfortunate, however, if teachers and students always stop "reading" at this most basic level of comprehension. Higher levels of comprehension—interpretation and application—should also be exercised. The sequence which follows the graph below will illustrate (with words) how questioning based on a graph may move through all levels of thinking/comprehension.

Going beyond the literal level, this graph could be used (and has been used) to introduce the concepts of inflation, of social legislation, and of socialized medicine.

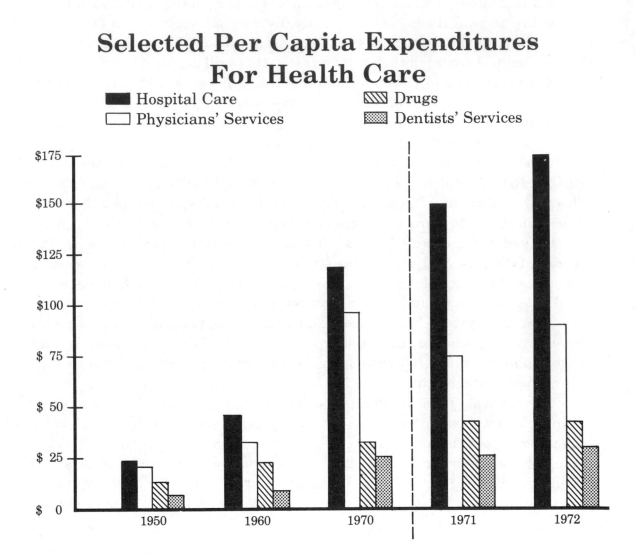

Selected Per Capita Expenditures For Health Care

Source: *Journal of Medical Education* 49 (Jan., 1974), p. 9.

Class discussion based on the graph

1. **What is the title of the graph?**
It is always important to call attention to the title of a graphic since this establishes the main idea and indicates purpose. This is a point to be kept in mind when producing one's own visuals—always entitle them. Though the content and meaning of a graph or chart may be perfectly obvious to its creator, it may yet remain a mystery to another person unless a hint (like a title) is given.

2. **What does "per capita" mean?**
Some students won't know. Maybe no one responds. **Do you know any other words that begin with the same letters, c-a-p-i-t-a?** (Capital.) **What is a capital? Or, what is the first letter in every sentence called? What is the type of hat we wear that has a bill on it? If you had a guillotine work on you, what would it do to you?** (Decapitate you.) From this it can be established that "cap" refers to the "head." Therefore, "per capita" means "per head" or "per person."

3. Identify the separate elements. These are the details that support the main idea. **What do the solid black bars represent? What do the solid gray bars stand for? What kind of information is given across the bottom of the graph? What are the intervals? Is there a break in the sequence? How do you know? Or, how has the graph maker alerted you visually that there is a break in the pattern? What kind of data is being presented on the vertical scale? What are the intervals, or increments?** Although this series of questions may seem too easy and too time consuming to the teacher (who may be familiar with the graphic), students must be able to identify (perceive) the separate elements before they are ready to read the data. That is the next step in the sequence. And, again, in leading students through this kind of process the teacher is teaching not only the content, but a skill which might even transfer to other subject areas and to private reading since graphics have a high degree of similarity and occur so frequently.

4. **Approximately how much money was spent per person for hospital care in 1950? In 1960? How much was the increase in terms of dollars during those ten years? What was the PERCENTAGE of increase?** Too often this last question is the point at which questioning begins when discussing a graph with students. In order to answer this question, the student must mentally go through the entire sequence of questions listed above in order to collect enough data to answer. And it must be done quickly because the teacher may allow only a few seconds thinking-time before expecting an answer.

5. **How much money was spent on hospital care in 1970? What is the percentage of increase over the amount spent in 1960? Why do you think it increased so much? Let's use our local hospital as an example. Do you**

99

know whether any kind of building or expansion was done during the late sixties? (Many hospitals did expand during that time.) **Why?** Several answers may be given. Usually someone will say that more people wanted hospital care. **Why?** Many reasons may be suggested. Medicare may be mentioned. A major reason for hospital expansion in the 1960's was the fact that many people who previously could not afford hospital care began to seek medical attention. Building materials and labor costs were rising, too, which, in turn, increased the cost of building rooms, staffing them, and occupying them. This could lead into a discussion of inflation. It might also be mentioned that many hospitals added intensive care and cardiac units at that time which also increased costs due to advancing technology and specialized staffing. Most of this part of the discussion is generated from inferences based on the scant data presented on the graph. It could lead into hypothesizing future costs based on trends established in the past. **Looking at the first two years of the 1970's what do you predict hospital costs will be in 1990 if this trends continues?**

6.   A similar analysis of physicians' services could be pursued. The topic of socialized medicine could easily arise. Several questions could be generated about this topic: **What countries do you know that have socialized medicine? What are the good (bad) features of such programs? What have been the responses to it in these countries? Who pays for it?** Most students won't have specific answers to these questions, but if they are interested, they could be led to do some reseach in the media center.

It is impossible to replicate an enthusiastic class discussion in print, but from the sample above, it might be seen that an entire class period can be (and has been) devoted to the reading, interpretation, and discussion of a rather simple graph. This particular one could be used in a nursing class, a social studies class, or a consumer economics class. It could be used as a lead-in to a particular topic, a chapter in a text, or to extended library research. No matter in what class or for what use, a line of questioning which requires reasoning skills to seek information beyond the literal level helps students develop skill in reading graphics while inquiring about subject matter.

Figure 1

TYPES OF GRAPHS AND HOW TO READ THEM

Graphs are visual representations of numerical data showing comparisons and relationships.

TYPES OF GRAPHS		DESCRIPTION AND PURPOSE	HOW TO READ THEM
LINE		Indicates precise relationship between two sets of data. Each point on the graph represents the two variables in relation to each other. Most accurate type of graph. Shows development taking place, trends.	1. Note title and type of graph. These indicate purpose, main idea.
BAR		Permits comparison of a small number of values (fewer than ten) taken at different times. Presentation may be made vertically or horizontally. Bars may be subdivided into parts of a whole or into percentages.	2. Note arrangement of data. Read column headings both vertical and horizontal to see what is being compared (dollars/year, pounds/acre, etc.).
3. Note scale. What are the increments of increase/decrease? Be alert to alterations within the pattern that can change appearance and cause misinterpretation.
CIRCLE or PIE		Shows how various parts relate to a whole; percentages.	4. Read the Key. It indicates the meaning of symbols. Color codes and surface patterns (cross-hatching dots, etc.) are often used.
5. Note symbols within the graph. These may be merely decorative, or may be meaningful components. (Consult the Key.)
SOLID FIGURE		Compares two or more *totals* using geometric figures to represent these quantities. Figures may be cubes, spheres, cylinders, etc.	6. Read for literal information.
7. Criticize. Make inferences, draw conclusions based on data. What applications are possible?
PICTURE or PICTO-GRAM		Illustrates approximate comparisons as bar graphs do, but uses representational figures like people, buses, cows or other items being compared.	8. Relate to text material.

The next example is a written exercise based on a chart taken from an elementary social studies textbook. Since the chart illustrates steps in a process, the exercise stresses this pattern of organization while also asking the child to relate some of these steps to his personal experience in order to develop the concept of profit which has been introduced and discussed in the body of the text.

Directions: Turn to the chart on page 66 of your textbook. Examine each section of the chart before answering the questions.

1. What kind of chart is this?
    _____ time chart
    _____ flow (sequence) chart
    _____ tree chart

2. Check the things you see on the chart:
    _____ airplane   _____ cans of food
    _____ truck   _____ mother cooking
    _____ farmer   _____ fish
    _____ policeman   _____ tractor

3. With these things in mind, check the title that best fits this chart.
    _____ Food Crops
    _____ Food: From Farm to Table
    _____ The Grocery Store
    Tell why you chose the title you did. _____
    _____

4. Does food go directly from the field to the table? Answer yes or no. _____

5. Tell three things the farmer does to his crops before they get to the factory. Put these in order as they happen.
    a. _____
    b. _____
    c. _____

6. What happens to the vegetables after they are canned or packaged and before they get to the warehouse?
    _____

7. What kinds of things must the person in charge of getting the vegetables from the factory to the warehouse have to think about before deciding what kind of transportation to choose? Is it better to send them by air, by truck, by ship, or what?
    _____
    _____
    _____

8. About how far do you think it might be from the warehouse to the grocery store? Why do you think so?
    _____

9. Check the things that the grocery clerk does when he gets the cans or packages of food.
    _____ sees how many are there   _____ takes them to the customer
    _____ unpacks them   _____ puts them on the shelves

10. What part does your family play in this process? Tell three things that you or someone in your family must do.
    a. _____
    b. _____
    c. _____

11. Does the farmer get his money from your family? Explain your answer.
    _____

12. Since food does not go directly from the farm to your home, how does this affect its price? Is the price higher or lower than the amount the farmer was paid for his crop? Why?
    _____
    _____

_____
[2]Developed by Sue Fort.

13. How are the people in the grocery store paid? Where does the money come from?

_____

14. Number these steps in the order that they happen.
    _____ Food is on the table.
    _____ Farmer grows the food.
    _____ Food goes to the warehouse.
    _____ The truck takes the crop to the packing house.
    _____ Mother cooks the food.
    _____ The food is put in cans and packages.
    _____ Food goes from the warehouse to the store.
    _____ Mother buys the food.
    _____ The grocery clerk puts the cans of food on the shelf.

A similar kind of exercise may be designed using a photograph. In the following example, the types of questions have been divided into levels which correspond to Gray's model of reading (see Chapter 1) and to Summers' suggestions regarding four types of skills students should be taught in order to read visual aids:

1. Recognize and interpret separate elements presented in visual aids. [*perception*]
2. Analyze and understand the relationships between elements contained in visual aids. [*comprehension*]
3. Pose questions and seek answers through the use of visual aids. [*reaction*]
4. Make inferences and draw conclusions from visual aids in light of the problem at hand.[3] [*application*]

---

[3]Edward G. Summers, "Utilizing Visual Aids in Reading Materials for Effective Learning," in *Developing Study Skills in Secondary Schools* ed. Harold L. Herber (Newark, Delaware: International Reading Association, 1965), p. 100.

[4]Post Wolcott. *Behind the bar;* Birney, Montana, 1941. Reproduced from the collection of the Library of Congress.

PART I
Check the items you see in the photograph.

_____ calendar
_____ sign
_____ flag
_____ patriotic banner
_____ gum ball machine
_____ cash register

PART II
Check two places this photograph is most likely to have been taken.

_____ private home
_____ airline terminal
_____ restaurant
_____ general store

PART III
Check the ideas you feel the photograph expresses.

_____ Prejudice cannot exist together with patriotism.
_____ Trust is the basis of good business relationships.
_____ Indians cannot be trusted with alcohol.
_____ Indians are poor credit risks.
_____ Other: _____

Choose one of these statements and tell why you agree (or disagree) that it expresses what you think the photograph means.

PART IV
Do one of the following:
1. Draw a cartoon expressing the theme of the photograph.
2. Write a caption for the photograph.
3. Write a short dialogue between the businessman who owns the establishment and an Indian who wants to buy beer on credit.

PRODUCING GRAPHICS

Once students have practiced reading and interpreting various kinds of graphics, they should be encouraged to produce their own. Putting into visual form the information gleaned from print requires understanding, attention to detail, selectivity, and a high degree of organization. If a student produces a good graphic based on text material, he has demonstrated what Piaget has termed "reversibility"—he has taken the concept apart and put it together again. This is a true test of comprehension.

---

[5]Developed by Nancy McGee.

Figure 2
TYPES OF CHARTS AND HOW TO READ THEM

Charts are visual summaries of important processes or relationships. They may combine pictorial, symbolic, numeric, and/or verbal elements.

TYPES OF CHARTS	DESCRIPTION AND PURPOSE	HOW TO READ THEM
FLOW	Illustrate a process, functional relationship, organization. Show simple or complex sequences.	1. Note title and type of chart. These indicate main idea and purpose. 2. Note symbols. These should be easily recognized. Do not attempt to read them literally. Notice details. Observe relationships. 3. Note pattern of organization: cause/effect, comparison/contrast, chronology, classification, step-by-step procedure, system. 4. Make inferences and draw conclusions based on data. 5. Relate to text material.
TREE	Show the way in which many things developed from one source; genealogies. Show development from root to many branches.	
TIME LINE	Show relations among events. Illustrate cause/effect, sequence. Multiple lines may be used to show overlapping events, depict zeitgeist.	
COMPARISON	Compare and contrast. Points may be listed side by side as advantages/disadvantages, pro and con. May be verbal or statistical.	
DIAGRAM	Show structure of a system (schematic), steps in a process, parts of a structure. Classify complex procedures. Many varieties—simple to complex.	

FIGURE 3

TYPES OF ILLUSTRATIONS AND HOW TO READ THEM

TYPES	DESCRIPTIONS	PURPOSES	HOW TO READ
PHOTOGRAPHS	Most realistic two-dimensional illustration. May be abstract, however. May be distorted due to selection, point of view, and/or editing.	Generate interest. Motivate. Clarify text by providing a sense of reality Effectively show step-by-step procedures; comparisons; status of things, processes, scenes, events, people.	1. Read title or caption. This may be misleading. If so, is there a reason? 2. Survey illustration, get general impression. 3. Look for details—objects, colors, symbols. Notice relationships. 4. Make inferences, draw conclusions, seek applications. 5. Refer to text in order to determine how to read illustration in terms of author's purpose for using it. 6. Report 4 (above).
PAINTINGS, DRAWINGS	Wide variety in type and style. Most realistic portrayal of pre-photography eras. Often found in history, literature and psychology texts. May provide interpretation of a scene, event, person. May represent abstract ideas, feelings, emotions.	Effectively demonstrate values, style, concerns of an era, group of persons, or individual. Compare and contrast values, styles, concerns of eras, groups of persons, individuals. Visual poetry.	
CARTOONS	Compact pictorial representations of ideas employing caricature, symbolism, exaggeration, humor, satire. Variety of artistic techniques. Frequently biased, distorted views. May employ symbols which can become out-dated because usually related to events, styles, thoughts of the era in which they appear. Rely on stereotypes. Purpose must be perceived in order to read the meaning.	Gain attention. Illustrate ideas, opinions. Criticize. Satirize. Prophesy. Introduce humor. Induce self-examination, self-criticism.	

In order to produce the graphic, the student will have had to read the text, select the main idea and supporting details, and perceive the relationship. Selection of an appropriate visual form into which to translate this relationship demonstrates understanding of the purposes which graphics serve and of the purposes to which the information to be presented can be put. The graphic form imposes the need for brevity with clarity. The student who has accomplished this task has read critically, thought critically, and organized his thinking.

KEY TO TEXTBOOKS—Graphics

Maps	Charts/Diagrams	Graphs
Burmeister, 221 Dechant, 279-285 Garland, 292-294; 298 Karlin, 232-234 Robinson, 195-197 Roe, 197-200 Shepherd, 117-126	Burmeister, 213-217 Dechant, 285-292 Robinson, 162-166; 197-198 Roe, 206 Shepherd, 127-128 Smith, 122-123	Burmeister, 224-227 Garland, 295-296 Karlin, 230-231 Robinson, 198-199 Roe, 200-205 Shepherd, 129-130 Smith, 121-122
Tables	Photographs/Cartoons	
Dechant, 292-293 Roe, 205 Shepherd, 128 Smith, 121-122	Burmeister, 219-221; 227 Herber, 120-124 Karlin, 234-235 Robinson, 202-203 Roe, 206-209 Shepherd, 130-131	

Because of the multiplicity of graphic materials in modern textbooks and because so much teaching and learning can be accomplished by putting these materials to good use, it is a field worthy of considerable attention. The selections listed below provide detailed information about graphics and include many illustrations and suggestions for using them.

Brown, James W., Richard B. Lewis, and Fred F. Harcleroad. "Graphic Materials," *AV Instruction: Media and Methods. 3rd ed.* New York: McGraw-Hill Book Company, 1969. 159-195.

Summers, Edward G. "Utilizing Visual Aids in Reading Materials for Effective Learning," *Developing Study Skills in Secondary Schools. Perspectives in Reading No. 4.* Edited by Harold L. Herber. Newark, Del.: International Reading Association, 1965. 97-155.

Wittich, Walter Arno, and Charles Francis Schuller, "Graphics" *Audiovisual Materials. 4th ed.* New York: Harper & Row, Publishers, 1967. 131-169.

ACTIVITY

Using the textbook of your choice, develop at least 10 sample questions for one example of each of the graphics listed. If a particular type of graphic is *not* included in your textbook, select examples from supplementary materials (newspapers are an excellent source) in order to complete the exercise. Such supplementary material should be related to your content area, however. Include questions in your exercises which require students to analyze, make inferences and draw conclusions. If possible, attach a copy of the graphic above the questions. Cite the source.

Exercise 6:
GRAPHICS

Photograph or Painting

Graph

Name _____

Chart

Diagram

Name _____

Cartoon

8

DEVELOPING STUDY SKILLS

RATIONALE

A student needs not only reading skills but also study skills. Too few students have skill enough to be able to establish purposes for their reading. As we have seen, having purpose is important in determining the rate at which the material should be read. With his purpose in mind and with book in hand, the good student plans his attack. But some students will need help at this point as well. Once the appropriate information has been obtained from the reading, the student may want to record the pertinent points to aid further recall. Does he know how to outline, or take notes, or summarize? Frequently he does not.

Each time a student is sent to the library to prepare for an oral or written report, he is in need of library reference skills. What materials will be useful to him? How are they to be found and used? Skimming and scanning skills are required in order to quickly find specific information. Having located it, he needs some method for making notes—outlining, writing precis, or other techniques. Then, with all information at hand, organizational skills are needed in order to prepare the report. Finally, students will need instruction in correct documentation.

When a student listens to a lecture or sees a demonstration, he needs good listening, observational, notetaking and summarizing skills in order to accurately record what he sees or hears for future reference.

Good work-study skills can become habits which will be found useful throughout life since they are efficient methods of learning how to learn. More is needed than good advice from well-meaning teachers and parents if students are to learn and actually practice these skills. They will be convinced that it is worth the trouble only when they see some improvement in their ability to do reading assignments, write reports, and recall information efficiently and accurately at exam time.

Teachers can insure such successes by providing students with instruction in how-to-do-it, then giving them many chances to practice study skills and ample opportunity to reap rewards in better performance and self-satisfaction for having taken the time to follow through. Indeed, research indicates that study skills *must* be directly taught and reinforced; otherwise, most students will neither learn them nor use them.

RATES AND PURPOSES FOR READING

Speed reading courses have become popular throughout the country, especially for those who have a great deal of reading matter to go through in a limited time. However, few content teachers will have time to devote to the development of speed reading skills, nor will there be many students who would greatly benefit from this instruction since skill in rapid reading should be taught only *after* the student has vocabulary, comprehension and reading skills that are well developed. For a person who may be called a *disabled reader* to attempt to increase reading speed to 2,000 words per minute would be no more reasonable than for a runner with a broken leg to attempt to beat the four-minute mile.

The mark of a poor reader is that he reads everything at the same rate. It might not occur to him that some things may be read faster, or that others should be read at a slower pace, depending on *why* he is reading. The content area teacher's purpose for developing rate should be limited to aiding students in becoming more *flexible* readers. To do this, they must become aware of the different types of reading rates and how these are related to common purposes of reading.

Intensive reading is studying. The reader wants to master detail, reflect upon what is written, and evaluate ideas. The purpose is to analyze or criticize. This is the slowest reading rate.

Casual reading is a little faster for it is the rate used when reading for recreation or pleasure. The reader may pause to enjoy a particular description or the writer's wit, but he doesn't slowly dissect each passage.

Accelerated reading is employed when time is short. The purpose is to seek understanding of main ideas and major details.

Selective reading is rapid reading in which the reader does not cover all material, but only those parts which serve his purpose. Scanning and skimming are two types of selective reading which can be developed in the content fields.

When **scanning**, the reader rapidly searches a page for a particular name, fact, or figure. This technique is used when looking for a number in the telephone directory, a name in an index, or a word in a glossary. The reader knows *in advance* what he is looking for. His eye scans a column or series of listings until it falls on the particular item he is searching for.

Skimming involves rapid coverage of an entire page, article, or chapter in order to pick up the gist of it. Details are omitted. It is helpful to skim difficult material prior to a very careful reading, or when reviewing after intensive reading in preparation for a test or to refresh one's memory. In this case, the reader is not looking for some specific item, but getting the essence of an entire selection.

Scanning exercises can be used to improve perceptual skills. Students often misread words which have similar configurations. This is evident if you listen to students read orally and hear them mispronounce "clothe" as "cloth" or transform "sliver" into "silver."

Scanning exercises to improve word perception are relatively easy to construct. Key words may be listed in a column on the left of the page. For each key word, select a word or words that have similar configuration and may, therefore, be easily confused with the key word. Mix the words that are different in a series which also contains repetitions of the key word. Place this series of words in a horizontal line to the right of the key word. Ask the student to mark the key word each time it occurs in the series. Specify a time limit. A list of fifteen words should take less than 35 seconds to complete. Words which have different initial consonants (fought, sought, ought), medial vowels (drink, drank, drunk), or final consonants (though, thought) should be included in the exercise for the sake of variety.

Sample Exercise: Scanning
Mathematics

Directions: This exercise contains some math terms you already know. But they may be easily confused because they look so much alike. The exercise is not to be graded. It is to help you recognize words quickly and accurately. At the signal, look at the word on the left and then continue reading along the line, circling or underlining each word that is the same as the first word in the line. You will have twenty-five seconds. Work as quickly as you can. If you finish before time is called, turn your paper face down on your desk.

1. fraction	faction	factor	fraction	faction	factor	fraction
2. radius	radius	radii	radical	radius	radii	radical
3. sector	section	section	sector	vector	section	sector
4. principal	principal	principal	principle	principle	principle	principal
5. exterior	exterior	interior	exterior	exterior	exterior	interior
6. inclusive	extensive	intensive	inclusive	extensive	inclusive	inclusive
7. spend	spent	spent	spent	spent	spend	spend
8. cycle	circle	cycle	circle	circle	cycle	cycle
9. congruent	congruent	component	conjugate	congruent	conjugate	congruent
10. attitude	altitude	attitude	altimeter	altitude	attitude	attitude

119

A variation of this type of exercise is to place a key word at the top of a column and list forty words (including the key word) which begin with the same letter under it. Ask the students to mark the key word each time it appears in the column. (It should appear several times.) A list of this length should take less than 20 seconds to scan.

Scanning practice using a variety of formats can be fun while also increasing students' proficiency. Drills can be devised based on telephone directories, catalogs, dictionaries, newspaper classified ads, reference materials, schedules of events (television lists, movie listings), and so forth.

Sample Exercise: Scanning
Newspaper Advertisement

Directions: Look at the advertisement. See how the information is arranged. Read the questions at the right, then go quickly through the advertisement to find the answers. You will be reading very quickly—just looking for specific bits of information. This kind of reading is called scanning.

1. How many miles on the Chrysler Cordoba?

2. What is the make and year of the least expensive car listed?

3. How many of these cars list air conditioning as a feature?

4. How many station wagons are advertised here?

5. How many of these cars are advertised as having bucket seats?

6. What is the difference in price between the two Datsun B-210's that are listed?

7. How much older is the one Olds Cutlass than the other one?

8. Which Ford Elite seems to be the best buy?

9. Which car is the oldest?

10. What are the makes and years of the two cars priced at $3688?

SAVE NOW!
Before The Price Increase

75 CHEVROLET CAMARO	2 dr., hardtop, auto. trans., power steering, air	$3688
75 CHEVROLET IMPALA	4 dr., hardtop, V8, auto. trans., power steering, air	$2888
77 DATSUN B-210	Hatchback, 5 speed trans., air, sharp	$3988
75 MERCURY COUGAR	2 dr., hardtop, V8, auto. trans., air, bucket seats	$3488
74 OLDS CUTLASS	2 dr., hardtop, V8, auto. trans., air, power, bucket seats	$2888
77 CHRYSLER CORDOBA	2 dr., hardtop, 9,000 miles, V8, auto. trans., air, power steering, bucket seats	$4888
75 DODGE CHARGER	2 dr., hardtop, V8, auto. trans., air, power steering, white with red bucket seats	$3288
76 PLYMOUTH ARROW	2 dr., hardtop, 4 speed, 4 cyl., blue w/blue seats	$2488
76 FORD ELITE	2 dr., hardtop, V8, auto. trans., air, yellow with white bucket seats	$3888
77 OLDS CUTLASS	2 dr., sharp, red w/white buckets, low mileage	$4988
76 FORD ELITE	2 dr., hardtop, V8, auto. trans., power, green with green bucket seats	$4288
75 FORD GRAN TORINO	Station wagon, V8, auto. trans., air, power	$2888
77 TOYOTA CELICA	GT, full power, with sun slots, very sharp	$5488
73 MG MIDGET	Convertible, 4 speed	$688
77 DATSUN B-210	4 speed, low mileage	$3288
74 PONTIAC TRANS AM	V8, auto. trans., all power, air, red with black bucket seats, sharp	$3688

Sample Exercise: Scanning
Telephone Directory

Directions: Using the overhead projector, we will be able to see on the screen, a page from our local telephone directory. Find the answers to the questions below as quickly as you can. Circle the correct answer on your paper. As soon as you finish, turn the paper over on your desk.

1. Find the phone number for John Webber.
   a. 898-4884   b. 475-9986   c. 365-0765

In this case, it is important for the student to notice that Webber *is spelled with two* b's. *There is a listing for a John Weber and his phone number is a possible choice as well.*

2. Gene Weaver's phone number is:
   a. 345-9645   b. 223-8564   c. 980-9923

There are many Weavers in the phone directory used for this exercise. The student first must find Weaver, then scan first names in order to find the correct listing. This exercise assumes that students know the alphabet. Many in the middle grades do not! In such a case, the teacher may wish to prepare exercises based on scrambled names or words in order to give these students practice in alphabetizing.

3. Charles West's business is manufacturing. What is his home address?
   a. 201 Brown St.   b. 1322 North Ave.   c. 1 Hill Dr.

There were four Charles West's listed in the directory. One had "mfg" after his name with first a business address then a home address listed. One of the addresses above is for the first Charles West listed in the directory; one is the business address of the Charles West in question; one is the correct home address.

Skimming exercises are also simple to plan. Newspaper features, magazine articles, and textbook chapters provide materials on which the exercises can be based. Instruct the students that skimming is systematic. First the title is read, then the first couple of sentences of the selection, next subtitles and lead sentences in the body, and finally the last two or three sentences. Knowledge of the organizational patterns used by authors increases skimming speed while aiding comprehension.

Begin with short pieces such as newspaper articles. Provide five or six questions of various types to test for literal comprehension. (Speed without comprehension is useless.)

In general, it should take students 30-45 seconds to skim a newspaper article; 60-75 seconds to skim a magazine article; and, 2-3 minutes to skim a textbook chapter. With practice, they can skim as well as answer the questions in these time periods. It is important that the student time himself on these exercises, but he should try to beat his own record, not anyone else's.

There are no established rates of speed for intensive, casual, accelerated or selective reading. Some students involved in casual reading will read at a faster pace than others who are involved in so-called accelerated reading. In all cases, *rate will be influenced by the individual reader's skills as well as his familiarity with the content field in which he is reading.* Students should realize this lest they become discouraged in attempting to improve rate. It bears repeating that the most important thing is to learn to *adjust* rate to purpose.

For students who are good readers and want to increase their speed, it is suggested that they go to a reading laboratory equipped with tachistoscopes, pacers and other devices designed for this purpose. Some schools offer a speed reading course as an elective for able students. Because good students frequently take this course, some of the stigma is removed from the reading laboratory which has often been thought of as a place where "dummies" have to go.

STUDY TECHNIQUES

There are a number of study techniques that content area teachers may share with their students. One of these has been named SQ3R (survey, question, read, recite, and review); another is PQ4R (preview, question, read, reflect, recite, and review); a third is PQRST (preview, question, read, state, and test).

As can be seen, the first step in these formalized study techniques is *previewing or surveying*. Previewing a reading assignment (for example, a chapter from the text) usually entails reading the title and subtitle (if any); then skimming the introductory paragraph; proceeding then to reading section headings, marginal headings, bold-face paragraph headings, or whatever means the author has used to show the organization of the material; and finally, skimming the summary paragraph. This provides the reader with an overview of the entire assignment.

The second step, then, is to pose questions for which one may reasonably expect to find answers in the process of reading the material more carefully. Teachers can help students to form the habit of posing questions by making it part of their own teaching technique. Questions can be printed in the form of a study guide, or the teacher may elicit questions from students through class discussion. One method is to turn the sub-headings, marginal headings, and paragraph headings into questions. For example, the sub-heading *Nature of Physical Environment* becomes, "What is the nature of the physical environment?" The information in that section of the text should provide answers to the question.

The third step in most study techniques is to *read carefully* in terms of the purposes that have been established and the questions that are to be answered. One way in which the teacher may help students read carefully is by designing exercises based upon the graphics, the new vocabulary, and stressing the organizational patterns within the text material. Such exercises will aid their comprehension of major concepts and important details in the reading. Exercises of this kind may be brought together in the form of a study guide.

The fourth step is to either *recite* or to *summarize* what has been read. Used as a teaching technique, this phase is usually accomplished through class discussions and in various activities requiring students to demonstrate their knowledge of the new material and their ability to apply it. Teachers can suggest that when studying alone, students attempt to answer their own questions and to summarize verbally or in writing what they have read in order to check their recall and understanding of the material.

The fifth and final step is to *review* or to *test*. Again, this may be a teacher-imposed or self-imposed activity. It usually culminates a series of reading assignments.

NOTE-TAKING SKILLS

Study skills should be directly taught where they are needed and when they are needed. Note-taking, outlining, and summarizing skills should be extended and reinforced in every class. This should not be left as the sole responsibility of the English teacher.

One way to reinforce formal outlining, once it has been directly taught, is to provide partially completed outlines of chapters, units, etc. These may be included in study guides. They may be used to direct homework assignments and to help students review for tests and examinations.

If a content area teacher has led students to perceive main ideas and organizational patterns of paragraphs, and has taught them how to "map" a reading assignment (see Chapter 6), then it will be much easier for them to produce organization in the form of notes, outlines, diagrams, or précis for whole selections.

Teaching students to write précis is seldom done even in English classes, yet it is an excellent way to help students develop skill in critical reading and writing. It may sound like a simple assignment to take a chapter or a long selection and to summarize it on one page or in one paragraph. But it takes skill to do it well. It is a skill that must be taught and practiced.

In order to write a précis, the reader must grasp the structure of the material and concentrate on essentials. Précis writing gives practice in close, attentive reading to find the main trend of thought, see the way it has been organized, identify key sentences, and accurately state major points that may have been implied. The reader must reduce explanatory and illustrative material to bare minimum while still preserving important details and examples. Essential

123

conditions, qualifiers, and distinctions must be preserved. Words like *if, unless, when, only,* and *almost* must be kept, and differences between *is, will,* and *might* must be noted in order to preserve accuracy. Finally, to write the précis, the most economical wording must be used while retaining the emphasis of the original by giving prominence to a point that was treated in detail, less emphasis to a point mentioned in passing.

REFERENCE SKILLS

Library reference skills should also be reinforced in all content areas. English teachers and librarians may be reasonably expected to provide basic instruction, but it will be necessary for content area teachers to call students' attention to the special reference materials important in the field of study and to provide practice in the use of these materials.

We may speak of *teaching* skills, but, in fact, skills are only *learned* through practice. And skills taught in English classes and in the media center will seldom become generalized unless they are put to use outside the context in which they were taught.

Librarians frequently complain that students tend to rely on encyclopedias, overlooking more complete, more timely media sources simply because they have never heard about them or don't know how to use them. It is not unusual for them to meet a student who has been sent to "do a report" on the Civil War, or on the hydronium ion, or on some aspect of geometry. Such a student too frequently has no instruction in how to proceed. He goes to *The World Book,* looks up "Civil War," and then comes to the librarian to say, "How come there's nothing in here about the Civil War?" After the student's attention has been directed to the cross-reference note which reads, "*see,* War Between the States," he turns to that entry, copies the first 500 words (if that is the length specified), and turns it in as a "report." Teachers who make such undirected assignments deserve what they get.

Assignments for work in the media center should be thoughtfully prepared. A report might be assigned which requires the student to answer a number of specific questions. Carefully wrought questions may make it necessary for the student to go to three or four sources, summarize the essential points in each, note discrepancies and varying points of view, apply his own intellect to problems which may arise, and finally incorporate all this into the final report. Students do not normally come by such skill without instruction and practice. But, the reward of receiving more interesting, better prepared reports from more interested, better prepared students, is worth the teaching time.

INFORMAL READING INVENTORIES

This book has attempted to give the reader an understanding of the fundamental reading skills which students must master and exercise in order to succeed in school work. Vocabulary and comprehension skills are important in every area and across the various content fields. But specific comprehension skills may be especially important in one field and less so in others. For example, social studies places a good deal of emphasis on chronology and on comparison and contrast. Physical education teachers are little interested in developing those skills, but they might want to be assured that students can follow sequence in reading rules and instructions and can interpret diagrams. The sciences rely on the noting of significant details and the interpretation of formulas. Both math and art deal with many graphics—although of different kinds. Reading skills are important in all areas and specific skills are important in each area to a greater or lesser extent. It is up to the teacher to determine which skills are most important to the conduct of the class.

Some skills may be important to a certain group of students; some may have significance at a given time. A mathematics teacher who has a class of bright students who need to consult tables frequently may want to insure that they can scan quickly. For classes which have been provided with a text having a good many special features, it may be important to stress the use of the various book parts.

Having determined which specific skills are important, the teacher will want to know, early in the course, which students already possess these necessary skills and which do not have them.

Most standardized reading tests give the teacher very little information about a student's ability to read specialized content. In order to fill this gap, the teacher may prepare an informal reading inventory based on the text and/or materials used in the class. It may be a good idea to administer such an inventory in the first few days of a new term. It will take no longer than one class period. The purpose for doing it is to give *this* teacher in *this* class a clear idea of how well *each* student can handle *these* materials. The kinds of questions to be asked in the informal reading inventory are of the sort described throughout this workbook.

In the following reprint, David L. Shepherd describes in some detail how informal reading inventories may be constructed. The example is based on an English literature text.

CONSTRUCTING GROUP READING INVENTORIES[1]

English—Group Reading Inventory

Directions for the diagnostic survey test are based on an English literature textbook.

I. Use between 34-40 questions.
II. Use questions designed to measure the following reading skills in the proportions shown below.
   A. Using parts of the book (3 questions in all)
     1. Table of Contents
     2. Index of Titles
     3. Glossary
     4. Biographical Data
     5. Introductory paragraph to story
   B. Vocabulary needs
     1. Meaning (7-8 questions)
       a. General background of word meanings
         (1) select correct meaning from several dictionary meanings
         (2) antonyms, synonyms
       b. Contextual meanings
     2. Word recognition and attack (14-15 questions)
       a. Divide words into syllables
       b. Designate the accented syllable
       c. Note and give meaning of prefixes and suffixes
       d. Changing the part of speech of a word (noun to verb, adjective to adverb, etc.)
   C. Comprehension (11-12 questions)
     1. Noting the main idea
     2. Recalling pertinent supporting details
     3. Drawing conclusions, inferences
     4. Noting the sequence of ideas
   D. Reading rate. Have student note the time it takes for him to read the selection. Then, figure reading speed in words per minute.
     Example: Words in selection: 4000
            Time to read: 10 minutes

$$\frac{4000}{10} \quad \text{equals} \quad 400 \text{ words per minute}$$

     Time may be recorded by student noting clock time for starting and stopping or by teacher recording time on blackboard every 30 seconds (1′, 1′30″, 2′, etc.)
   E. Skimming to locate information (2-5 questions)
     Use selection different from the one used for comprehension and speed purposes.
III. Choose a reading selection of not more than four pages.
IV. In administering the inventory:
   A. Explain the purpose of the inventory and the reading skills it is designed to measure. When the inventory is given, advise the students which skill is being measured.
   B. Read each question twice.
   C. Questions on the use of the parts of a book are asked first. Students will use their books.
   D. Introduce the reading selection, establishing necessary background on the topic and giving the students a question to guide their reading.
   E. Read selection silently. Note and figure speed.
   F. Ask questions on vocabulary. Students will use book for questions measuring ability to

---

[1]David L. Shepherd, *Comprehensive High School Reading Methods, 2nd ed.* (Columbus, Ohio: Charles E. Merrill Publishing Company, 1978), pp. 24-27. Used with permission of the publisher. See also pp. 27-33 for directions for social studies, science and mathematics inventories.

determine meaning from context. They will not use the book for other vocabulary questions, and these should be written on the blackboard.

    H.   Skimming. Use a new selection. Books will be used.

   V.   A student is considered to be deficient in any one specific skill if he answers more than one out of three questions incorrectly, or more than two incorrectly when there are more than three questions measuring a specific skill.

  VI.   This inventory, being administered to a group, does not establish a grade level. Nonetheless, anyone scoring above 90 per cent may be considered to be reading material too easy for him. Anyone scoring below 65 per cent may be considered to be reading material too difficult for him. If the material is suitable, the scores should range between 70-90 per cent.

 VII.   . . . tabulation of results . . .

VIII.   Sample Form of Inventory.

Parts of book

1. "On what page does the unit (section) entitled *Exploring One World* begin?"
2. "What section of your book would you use to find out something about the author of a story in the book?"
   (Determines knowledge of section on biographical data.)
3. "In what part of the book can you find the meaning of a word that you might not know?" (Determines knowledge of glossary.)

Introduce

Explore student background of experiences on the subject of the story and set up purpose questions. Students read silently. Time required is noted.

Vocabulary

4. "What is meant by the word *crab* as it is used in the story (line _____, column _____, page _____)?"

Contextual

5. "What is meant by the word *eliminated* (line _____, column _____, page _____)?

Synonyms and antonyms

6. "What word means the opposite of *temporary?*"
7. "Use another word to describe the coach when he looked amazed."

General knowledge of meaning

8. "Select the proper meaning of the word *entice.*"
   a. to lure, persuade
   b. to force
   c. to ask
   d. to caution
9. "Select the proper meaning of the word *initial.*"
   a. the last or end
   b. the beginning or first
   c. the middle
   d. a letter of the alphabet
10. "Select the proper meaning of the word *rectify.*"
    a. to do wrong
    b. to make right
    c. to destroy
    d. a priest's home

Word Recognition: "Divide the following words into syllables and show which syllable is accented:"

accents

11—12. eliminated
13—14. amazed
15—16. undemocratic
17—18. fraternities

Prefixes suffixes

19. "What does the prefix *un* mean as used in *undemocratic?*"
20. "What is meant by *pre* in the word *pre*scription?
21. "Change the verb *astonish* to a noun."
22. "Change the noun *boy* to an adjective."
23. "Change the adjective *democratic* to a noun."
24. "Change the adjective *slow* to an adverb."

Comprehension:	25.	"What is a _____? What happened when _____?"
main ideas;	26.	(Such questions as applicable here; ask for
	27.	only the main points of the story.)
details	28.	(Questions to ask for specific bits of information
	29.	about the principal characters or
	30.	ideas of the material.)
Drawing	31.	(Questions, the answers to which are not completely
conclusions;	32.	found in the textbook. Questions beginning with "why,"
inferences	33.	making comparisons, or predicting what may happen. e.g. "Why did Bottle imagine he could perform such astounding athletic feats as setting the state high school record in jumping?")
Sequence	34.	(May be omitted.) Questions asking what happened as
	35.	a result of _____, what steps did the police use to solve the mystery, etc.
Skimming		
	36.	Use a new reading section (Questions designed to
	37.	have the pupil locate some specific bit of information)

ANALYSIS CHART FOR GROUP INFORMAL READING INVENTORIES

A detailed format for analysis of the group informal reading inventory is shown on the next page. It was designed to accompany an inventory of social studies skills; therefore, skills groupings might have to be adjusted for other content areas.

General instructions for using the Analysis Chart Are:

1. List students' names in a column at the left.
2. Group questions included on the informal reading inventory according to skills. List these skills across the top of the page.
3. Underneath each skills category, provide a narrow column for each question included in the category. Number the columns to correspond with the numbering of the test items.
4. Place a check mark under the number of the question which was missed and alongside the name of each student who missed it.

The result will be a scattergram which may be found useful in choosing skills for all-class study, or for the formation of smaller skills groups, and so forth.

ANALYSIS CHART FOR GROUP INFORMAL READING INVENTORY—SOCIAL STUDIES

Name of Student	Using Parts of the Book					Using Source Materials				Using Maps and Charts				Under-standing Vocabulary				Noting Main Ideas			Noting Details			Drawing Conclu-sions		Noting Organi-zation	
	1	2	3	4	5	6	7	8	9	10	11	12	13	14	15	16	17	18	19	20	21	22	23	24	25	26	27

KEY TO TEXTBOOKS—Study Skills

Background	Study Techniques	Rate
Burmeister, 100-104 Dilner, 68-71 Karlin, 205-209 Smith, 251-252; 278-280	Aukerman, 59-61 Burmeister, 104-108 Dechant, 273-279 Dilner, 71-73 Forgan, 227-250 Hafner, 177-182 Thomas, 136-168 Roe, 175-179 Shepherd, 112-113 Smith, 252-258	Aukerman, 80-83 Burmeister, 296-314 Dechant, 316-334 Dilner, 81-83 Karlin, 235-247 Olson, 90-99 Thomas, 195-234 Robinson, 284-287; 290-291 Roe, 209-213 Shepherd, 134-136 Smith, 258-262
Notetaking	**Using Sources of Information**	**Test Taking Skills**
Dechant, 260-268 Dilner, 78-81 Garland, 297 Hafner, 173-177 Karlin, 219-225 Olson, 43-44 Thomas, 267-275 Robinson, 207-210; 223-224 Roe, 179-185 Shepherd, 113-116 Smith, 262-267	Burmeister, 318-338 Dilner, 73-76 Garland, 290-294 Hafner, 161-173 Karlin, 228 Thomas, 244-258 Roe, 185-188; 190-192 Shepherd, 131-134 Smith, 270-276	Hafner, 181-183 Roe, 215-216
Informal Reading Inventories		**Study Skills Tests**
Aukerman, 11-12 Burmeister, 46-55 Dechant, 350-352 Dilner, 96-106 Estes, 68-94 Forgan, 101-133	Garland, 241-251 Hafner, 77-84 Karlin, 83-90; 95-104 Robinson, 36-63 Shepherd, 23-34 Smith, 122-134; 138-140	Estes, 104-115 Hafner, 72-77

See Also:

Courtney, Brother Leonard, F.S.C. "Organization Produced," *Developing Study Skills in Secondary Schools. Perspectives in Reading No. 4.* Edited by Harold L. Herber. Newark, Del.: International Reading Association, 1965. 77-96.

Shepherd, David L. "Using Sources of Information," *Developing Study Skills in Secondary Schools. Perspectives in Reading No. 4.* Edited by Harold L. Herber. Newark, Del.: International Reading Association, 1965. 42-56.

ACTIVITY

Using the textbook of your choice, prepare an informal reading inventory. Base 25 to 40 questions upon the material. Ask questions in at least eight categories of reading/study skills. Some examples are: using book parts, understanding technical vocabulary, recognizing prefixes and suffixes, picking out main ideas, noting details, drawing conclusions, applying formulas or theoretical information, following directions, noting organization, interpreting graphics, using source materials, etc.

You may, if you wish, select some items from the exercises you have written previously in Chapters 4-7.

Prepare an analysis chart to accompany the informal reading inventory. (See the sample with instructions for preparation on pages 128 and 129).

Exercise 7:
GROUP READING INVENTORY
AND ANALYSIS CHART

9

PREPARING READING ASSIGNMENTS

DAILY READING DEMANDS

Though most of the skills discussed thus far are vital in aiding students to use text materials efficiently, the majority of the time spent with such materials will be for the sake of learning facts and ideas rather than for developing skills *per se*. Each subject area has characteristic material which is likely to involve unusual formats, an abundance of factual matter, and numbers of complex concepts compressed into a small area. As a result, students must possess a variety of reading and study skills in order to elicit the key issues in each discipline and to establish patterns of relationships within their own minds.

Consider a typical school day. During a first period mathematics class, a student may be reading terse symbolic mathematical language to understand mathematical concepts and practice mathematical skills. He might be required to translate "story problems" into mathematical language in order to set up formulas and similar constructs. The next hour he may be in a social studies class where he could be required to distinguish fact from opinion, or, in a research paper, to trace the development of an historical sequence through cause and effect, or to relate how climate influences culture through comparative reading of maps. Third period he might have to struggle through a long poem, attempting to straighten out inverted, complex sentence structure to find the literal meaning, while trying to figure out the symbolic meaning. At the same time, he may have to state how meter, rhyme scheme, and other poetic devices enchance the "real" meaning of the poem. Next he may saunter into a chemistry class where, in order to set up lab equipment, he may be required to follow explicit directions. Then he is likely to have to read chemical symbols in order to conduct the experiment.

After lunch he may go to band where he reads yet another specialized symbol system with key signatures, time indications, Italian phrases for proper interpretation, musical notes, and the director's non-verbal language. In each class, the student is required to do some reading, yet, each course, by its very nature, imposes a unique set of reading skills.

As specialists in a particular field, teachers have refined their own skills through years of study to such an extent that these have become second-nature. They may tend to forget that these skills are likely to be entirely new to their students. Further, they often fail to consider the number and diversity of skills students must use daily with a fair degree of proficiency in order to master the curriculum.

The most successful teachers are often those who assume least about what students already know and who direct students' attention to special requirements of the material to be used here and now. Such teachers satisfy themselves that the students are prepared to handle specific reading assignments before the assignment is made. To do this, some time is spent preparing the reading assignments through a careful content analysis.

CONTENT ANALYSIS

The steps in preparing a reading assignment may seem familiar. The procedure is similar to that of developing lesson plans. The difference lies in shifting the focus from *teaching content* to teaching *how to read and understand* content. Here is an outline of the steps:

I. Read the chapter carefully
   A. Determine major concepts presented
      1. through technical terms
      2. through visual aids provided
   B. Determine which words are essential—words that students must know in order to understand the concepts.
      1. general
      2. special
      3. technical
   C. Determine the predominant organizational pattern of the chapter
      1. chronological
      2. listing
      3. comparison/contrast
      4. cause/effect
      5. combination of the above

D. Determine skills students need
    1. to unlock meaning of vocabulary words
    2. to follow organization and understand concepts
    3. to apply or transfer concepts
E. Determine necessary background information and interesting ways to present it.
    1. media
    2. speaker
    3. lecture
    4. simulation
    5. field trips
    6. other

II. Establish objectives

III. Plan initial activities
  A. Order films, prepare media, engage speaker for background and/or motivation
  B. Prepare materials
  C. Preview reading with students

The first step, that of carefully reading the material to be assigned, seems so obvious that it hardly needs mentioning. However, teachers who have been teaching from a particular book for a few years often do not reread the chapters when preparing to teach them and frequently *assume* that a great deal more information is in the text than is actually there. However, it is *how* the teacher reads the chapter that is perhaps the most important aspect in the teaching of reading for it is through careful analysis that the teacher will determine what is to be taught and what skills students need to learn. As Vacca states, "The bulk of effective 'reading instruction' in the content areas may very well come before the students read—during the preparation component of a teacher's lesson."[1] It is during this careful reading of the chapter that the teacher is doing the content analysis, which is described by the items listed in the outline above under Roman numeral I.

In analyzing the chapter, the teacher is, essentially, asking a series of questions. What are the important concepts? If a concept is a process, is there a chart or diagram which presents the process visually? If so, should the focus of the initial discussion be on the chart or diagram? (Chapter 7 discussed the use of graphic materials.)

What technical vocabulary words are used to describe the concepts? What are the relationships between and among these words? That is, do the meanings of

---

[1]Richard T. Vacca, "Readiness to Read Content Areas Assignments," *Journal of Reading, 20* (Feb., 1977), p. 390.

some words have to be known first because they become essential components in the definitions of other terms? What would be the best way to teach these vocabulary words? (Chapter 5 was devoted to this important topic.)

How is the information presented? That is, what is the author's predominant organizational pattern? Is he primarily comparing or contrasting? Is he instructing how to do something using a step-by-step procedure? How much and what kind of background does the student need to have in order to understand this information? Is the student asked to draw conclusions? Will he have to demonstrate his knowledge by applying the information (or procedures) in another situation? If a number of steps or ingredients are involved, must the student remember them in a particular order? (Such questions deal with comprehension and critical reading. These topics were addressed in Chapter 6).

The answers to these questions and ones like them will determine the objectives to set for a reading assignment and the activities and materials to be developed in order to aid the students in meeting these objectives.

After the initial planning, and preparation of materials, the teacher must prepare the *students* for the reading assignment. Too many teachers simply write the assignment on the board, or shout it out after the bell rings while students are scrambling for the door. Even when care is taken that students hear the assignment and make note of the pages, they often don't know what to *do*. Simply telling them to read pages 116 through 146 is not enough. It is important that students know the teacher's purposes for assigning the material. This helps them to decide *how* to read it. Should they read in order to obtain an overview, or should they read to remember particular points or concepts? Will they have to compare what they read tonight with what they read last night? How does the reading relate to what they did in class today or will do in class tomorrow? Does the reading reinforce what has already been discussed, or is it meant to introduce new ideas?

A teacher may find it useful to devise a chart similar to the one on the facing page as an aid in doing content analyses of reading assignments. This particular chart has been used by a social studies teacher to analyze a chapter about conservation.

CONTENT ANALYSIS

CONTENT AREA	Social Studies
CHAPTER	Conservation of natural resources

MAJOR CONCEPT(S)	CONTENT TOPICS

Conservation	I. Types of Conservation
	II. Conservation Projects
	  A. Dams
	  B. Irrigation Projects
	  C. Urban Renewal
	III. Public Lands and Resources
	  A. National Parks
	  B. State Parks

VOCABULARY	ORGANIZATIONAL PATTERN
Erosion Terracing Habitat Watershed Irrigation Predators Runoff Plant cover Sustained yield	Comparison and contrast Chronological Listing

SKILLS NEEDED	VISUAL AIDS
Map reading Using charts and tables Reading graphs Note-taking Distinguishing fact and opinion	Photos of erosion pp. 62, 63, 64 Chart: Water Conservation p. 70 Maps pp. 65, 67, 69

RESOURCES FOR BACKGROUND AND MOTIVATION

PEOPLE	PLACES	MEDIA	OTHER

County Agricul-
  tural Agent
4-H sponsor
Audubon Society
  President
Forest Ranger
	County Park
	State Park
	National Park
	Tree Farm
		Teacher-made
		slide tape
		presentation
		Film:
		Disappearing
		Wildlife-County
		Media Center-30
		minutes	

STRUCTURED OVERVIEW

One of the major purposes in introducing the reading assignment is to relate the new information to the old information, that is, relating the known to the unknown. One of the primary jobs of any teacher is to lead the student to discover what he already knows about a "new" topic by helping him to clearly organize previous knowledge. David Ausubel, a learning theorist, worked with this idea and decided that a person's knowledge falls into a pattern which is often organized in terms of a hierarchy from generalized concepts to specific facts. As a result, he recommends that "advance organizers" be used to help students learn and retain new concepts. Advance organizers help them to get cognitively "ready" for new concepts by providing a framework of known concepts to support the new details, thus extending the framework to include a new concept.

A kind of advance organizer used by reading teachers to get students ready to read is called a "structured overview." Structured overviews are visual diagrams of the relationships between key concepts (vocabulary) already known by the students and those to be learned. The notion of making a diagram or graphic representation of ideas is important since it concretizes the relationship between and among ideas. This not only helps students to learn new material, but it also helps them to remember it. As Jerome Bruner, another learning theorist, noted in *Process of Education,* "Perhaps the most basic thing that can be said about human memory, after a century of research, is that unless detail is placed in a structural pattern, it is rapidly forgotten" (p. 24).

Devising a structured overview of a chapter is somewhat simplified if a careful content analysis of the chapter has been done. After the vocabulary has been selected, the list is arranged in the form of a diagram which illustrates the relationships. A transparency, a dittoed reproduction, or a chalkdrawing of the diagram might be presented to the students as an introduction to the chapter.

Here is an example of a structured overview based upon the same chapter about conservation for which the content analysis was done on page 139.

STRUCTURED OVERVIEW

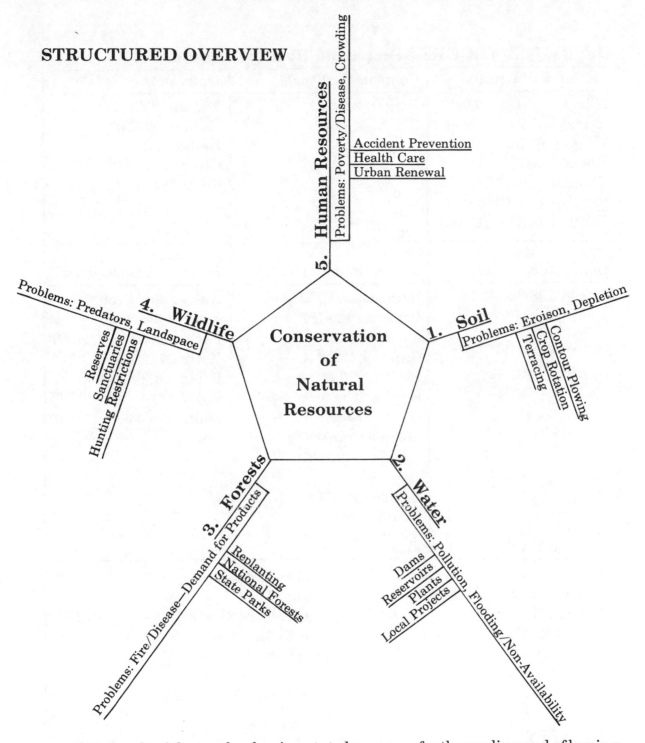

As a result of the teacher having stated purposes for the reading and of having presented a structured overview, students should be able to approach the reading assignment with some notion of the concepts to be encountered, the words used to describe these concepts, the relations between the new concepts and those they already know, and what specific points to look for in their reading—that is, what to *do* while they are reading.

KEY TO TEXTBOOKS—Preparing Reading Lessons

Selecting Materials	Content Analysis	Motivation
Dilner, 133-135; 171-181 Estes, 34-35 Forgan, 67-98 Olson, 35-87 Thomas, 125-136 Shepherd, 171-174 Smith, 343-349; 355-366	Herber, 229-231 Smith, 318-319	Forgan, 253-329 Hafner, 497-500 Herber, 173-189 Olson, 159-164 Smith, 84-100

Diagnostic/Prescriptive	Grouping/Individualizing	Prereading/ Structured Overviews
Dilner, 198-224	Burmeister, 109-113 Dechant, 125-132 Estes, 126-132 Garland, 222-241 Herber, 200-212 Karlin, 285-301 Olson, 216-224 Robinson, 267-268; 278-279 Roe, 49-53 Shepherd, 159-171 Smith, 392-406	Aukerman, 45-59 Estes, 142-152 Herber, 147-149; 152-158 Karlin, 111-117 Robinson, 68-85 Roe, 59-61 Smith, 300-307; 315-316

Directed Reading Lessons/Units	
Aukerman, 87-97 Burmeister, 94-100; 113-117 Dilner, 141-164 Estes, 132-137 Forgan, 205-218 Garland, 192-221	Herber, 213-229 Karlin, 117-127 Olson, 44-59; 118-124; 128-138; 139-158 Roe, 61-68; 73-76 Shepherd, 137-157 Thomas, 101-124 Smith, 153-154; 307-315

ACTIVITY

Using a textbook of your choice, do a content analysis of a chapter or unit and prepare a structured overview. Provide a written comment to accompany the structured overview which will clarify the context and/or frame of reference.

You may wish to plan ahead to use this structured overview as the basis for the preparation of a study guide. Study guides are discussed in the next chapter.

Exercise 8:
CONTENT ANALYSIS

Name _____

CONTENT AREA

CHAPTER

MAJOR CONCEPT(S)	CONTENT TOPICS

VOCABULARY	ORGANIZATIONAL PATTERN

SKILLS NEEDED	VISUAL AIDS

RESOURCES FOR BACKGROUND AND MOTIVATION

PEOPLE	PLACES	MEDIA	OTHER

10

DESIGNING STUDY GUIDES

RATIONALE

The exercises in this book have been designed to encourage teachers (or prospective teachers) to practice developing various types of exercises which may help students gain the skills they need in order to succeed in their classes. Of necessity, these skills have been discussed one at a time; however, in an actual teaching situation, several may be brought into play simultaneously—in discussions, in the process of giving instructions, in working on class projects, in working through teacher-made study guides.

Study guides may vary in length, emphasis, and format depending on the type of reading assignment or the type of skills required in order to complete the assignment. The study guide is a useful tool for the teacher who has students of varying abilities since group assignments may be made for various parts of the guide when each part has been designed to emphasize a distinct skill or to recognize various levels of comprehension. It is not always necessary for everyone to do all of the activities included in the study guide. This approach permits the teacher to obtain responses from all students in a heterogeneously grouped class since there is a level at which each student is *able* to respond. Each will have something to contribute to a discussion of the topic. In a homogeneously grouped class, dividing the work may make it possible to obtain wider, or more in-depth coverage of a topic by letting small groups work separately and then contribute their findings in a whole class discussion.

An analysis of an informal reading inventory (as described in Chapter 8) is one way to identify the skills needed by the group as a whole and by individuals and small groups. These skills can then be stressed in the study guide.

145

PUTTING THE STUDY GUIDE TOGETHER

The best study guides frequently include a number of elements: vocabulary exercises, comprehension exercises based on both graphic and verbal material, exercises that stress patterns of organization, use of various study skills, and enrichment activities. These exercises and activities are presented in a variety of formats: diagrams, charts, and outlines to be completed, essays, short answers, fill-ins, matching, acrostics and other puzzles, true-false, multiple-choice, and so forth.

Vocabulary sections may be included when the assignment introduces a number of general, special, and/or technical vocabulary words. Organization may be stressed when the selection seems to be based on comparison/contrast, cause and effect, or other distinct patterns. If the selection contains an especially good graphic, this may form the basis for a series of questions which lead the student from the literal, to the interpretative, to applied levels of comprehension. Perhaps tables or charts are included which could form the basis of a scanning exercise. The skills to be emphasized depend upon the content to be learned.

Study guides may also include activities which involve students in projects, library research, or other investigations outside of the class, or outside of school. Through such enrichment activities students can directly relate what they have read to the world about them.

ENRICHMENT ACTIVITIES

In our society, skill in reading has value at the merely literal level of comprehension. It is a skill that readers use daily simply for preserving and continuing life. They respond accurately to messages like DANGER, KEEP LEFT, and TUNA SANDWICH 75¢. Those who read at the interpretive level may be able to go through school with a degree of success. But, it is at the level of *application/integration,* the highest level of comprehension, the final component in Gray's model of reading, that the reading/thinking process can make a qualitative difference in one's life. Information that has been obtained and new ideas that have been gleaned may become useful and enriching. Furthermore, a teacher's best indicator that a student fully comprehends concepts, processes, and information is that the student is able to put the information to use, to apply it in a new or different way, in his own way. It is thus the student best demonstrates that what has been taught has also been learned—that it has become his possession.

Enrichment activities provide opportunities for students to transfer and apply information obtained in class and through reading. Content teachers have long attempted to relate their subject matter to the real world by designing activities and

146

projects for students to *do*. Such activities pertain to the highest stage of the reading process—integration.

Students vary in the kinds of abilities they possess. So should enrichment activities vary if all students are to find ways to successfully bridge the gap from the book and the class to the real world. Enrichment activities may be especially needful for the gifted who are likely to become bored if their high level of interest is not met, but the less gifted need to bridge the gap, too. They, also, need to see how schooling relates to life.

Projects and activities may take a lot of time, or a little. They may be academic and theoretical, or strictly practical. They may require, in various proportions, verbal skill, manual dexterity, artistic ability, will-power, and brute strength and endurance. They may be home-related, school-related, community-related, or simply personal. Here are a few examples.

Plan, plant, care for a garden. Make a bedspread, a bread board, a model, a map. Compare the results of feeding a pair of rats, one on natural foods, one on "commercially prepared" foods. Do additional research in the media center. Design a mathematical table or chart to accompany an oral report to the class. Produce a film, a slide-tape presentation. Compose a poem; write a story. Interview a long-time resident, an artist, an Indian chief. Cook a foreign food, or a snack, for all the class to sample. Enter a project in the fair. Write a letter-to-the-editor. Visit a museum, or a grocery store, or a shoe factory; then, write a description, or prepare an oral report. Write, direct and/or perform in a play. Go on a diet, or swim twenty laps every day for a month, and chart progress.

Asked about their best memories of school, many adults report a project they did; a paper they wrote. The elements which made it a good experience probably include: they were given a choice, it was interesting, they knew or were given direction how to go about it, it took a lot of effort, and it was a success—a personal achievement.

SAMPLE STUDY GUIDE[1]

Title of Textbook: <u>Consumer Economic Problems</u>
Title of Chapter: <u>Understanding and Using Credit</u>
Length of Chapter: <u>16 pages</u> Approximate Reading Time: <u>45 minutes</u>

Background information and ways to introduce the reading:

The day before the chapter is to be introduced, students will be asked to skim through the chapter. (They have been doing this for previous chapters.) They will be reminded to read the title, the first couple of sentences, the subtitles and lead sentences, and finally, the last few sentences. They will be told that Mr. Chaffiot, president of the local Credit Bureau, will be coming the following day to speak on the topic of consumer credit. The students will be advised that they will have a chance to ask him questions. In skimming the chapter they will be expected to formulate some questions to put to him. He will be bringing pamphlets to distribute to the class. These pamphlets contain short discussions about how young adults may go about obtaining and using credit.

On the day following the visit by Mr. Chaffiot, a short color film strip will be shown, entitled, *The Consumer and Credit.* This will review material presented the previous day.

On the third day, a structured overview will be presented in order to introduce the reading assignment. The study guide will be distributed and group assignments will be made. Groups will work together to find and compare answers and to resolve difficulties.

Objectives:

1. Students will skim the chapter.
2. Students will demonstrate interest in the topic by asking questions of the guest speaker.
3. Students will read the chapter.
4. By satisfactorily completing the assigned portions of the study guide, students will
   a. demonstrate knowledge of the specialized vocabulary.
   b. develop an understanding of the essentials and uses of credit.
   c. verbalize their own feelings about charge accounts.
   d. formulate their opinions regarding credit, in general.
   e. identify the major concepts relative to consumer credit.
5. Students will be able to draw some conclusions regarding consumer credit through class discussion and/or in a short writing assignment.

Study Guide:

Part A—Vocabulary Exercise #1

Directions: Read each sentence carefully. Take note of the italicized words. Below the sentences are two columns. In the column at the left are words which you must compare to the column containing possible meanings. Select the meaning which best fits the context of the sentence in which the word was found.

SENTENCES

1. *Credit* is an advance of money or of goods and/or services in exchange for a promise to pay at a later time.
2. Another term for earning power is *capacity*.
3. A business firm that holds a 60-day note, may decide to take it to a bank and *discount* it; that is, to sell it for less than its value at maturity.
4. In the vocabulary of economics, *capital* refers to the money and property (except raw materials) owned or used by business.

---

[1]Developed by Joan L. DiTonno

148

Structured Overview—
UNDERSTANDING AND USING CREDIT

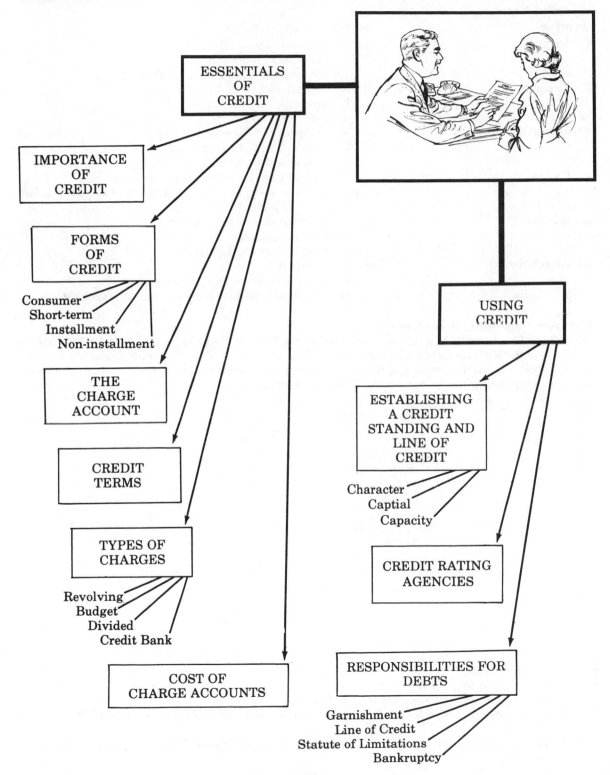

ESSENTIALS
OF
CREDIT

IMPORTANCE
OF
CREDIT

FORMS
OF
CREDIT

Consumer
Short-term
Installment
Non-installment

THE
CHARGE
ACCOUNT

CREDIT
TERMS

TYPES OF
CHARGES

Revolving
Budget
Divided
Credit Bank

COST OF
CHARGE ACCOUNTS

USING
CREDIT

ESTABLISHING
A CREDIT
STANDING AND
LINE OF
CREDIT

Character
Captial
Capacity

CREDIT RATING
AGENCIES

RESPONSIBILITIES FOR
DEBTS

Garnishment
Line of Credit
Statute of Limitations
Bankruptcy

5. A *minor* is a person who is not yet old enough to be considered legally responsible according to the laws of the state.

6. A legal process whereby property is taken under the control of the court until a case is settled is called *attachment*.

WORDS		POSSIBLE MEANINGS
1. Credit	1.	a. praise or approval
		b. favorable reputation
		c. trust in one's integrity and ability to pay
2. Capacity	2.	a. mental ability
		b. aptitude
		c. earning power
3. Discount		a. disbelieve or disregard entirely
		b. to take less than face value
		c. to lessen the effect of
4. Capital	4.	a. wealth used by a business to make a profit
		b. a city or town that is the official seat of government
		c. most important
5. Minor	5.	a. lesser in size or importance
		b. under legal age
		c. a secondary field of study
6. Attachment	6.	a. devotion
		b. something additional, an accessory
		c. taking of a person, property, etc. into custody

Part A—Vocabulary Exercise #2

Directions: This exercise is based on specialized terms found in the chapter. As you read the chapter, take note of the *italicized* words. To solve the puzzle, read the definitions below. Think of the word (or words) which fits the definition and has the same number of letters as the number of spaces provided in the corresponding line of the puzzle. Write the word in.

```
 1.        C H A R G E   _ C _ _ _ _ _
 2.      _ _ _ _ _ _ _ _   R _ _ _ _
 3.          _ _ _ _ _   E _ _   C R E D I T
 4.              _ _ _ D _ _   _ _ _ _ _ _
 5.            _ _ _ _ I _ _ _ _ _ _
 6.          _ _ _   _ _ _ T _ _ _ _ _   _ _ _ _ _ _
 7.        _ _ _ _ _ _ _   T _ _ _ _ _
 8.            _ _ _ E _ _ _ _
 9.          _ _ _ R _ _ _ _
10.      _ _ _ _ _ _ _ M _ _ _ _
11.          _ _ _ _ I _ _ _
12.      _ _ _ _ _ _ _   _ _ N _   P L A N
13.  _ _ _ _ _ _ _ _   _ _ O _ _ _
14.  _ _ _ _ _ _ _ _   O F   L _ _ _ _ _ _ _ _ _
15.          _ _ _   O _ _ _ _ _   _ _ _ _ _ _   _ _ _ _ _ _ _
16.        _ _ _   G - _ _ _ _   _ _ _ _ _ _
17.          _ Y _ _ _   _ _ _ _ _ _ _
```

1. An open account.
2. Credit granted to a consumer.
3. A loan which must be repaid within a short time.
4. Cooperative association for pooling savings of members and making loans to them at a low rate of interest.
5. Notice from the court that a debtor's property may not be disposed of until claims of creditors are settled.

150

6. Type of credit in which it is agreed that repayment of the full amount of the loan will be made at the specified date of maturity.
7. A person's reputation for paying bills, etc.
8. Money paid to a creditor for the privilege of using money, or of using goods prior to paying for them.
9. A type of long-term loan granted for the purpose of buying property or a home.
10. Payments which are to be made at specific intervals (often monthly).
11. Also called charge plates.
12. Agreement whereby the customer's bills are submitted to the bank for payment directly from the customer's account.
13. An account set up to pay for services rendered (legal, medical, etc.).
14. `Law which establishes a time limit after which a creditor cannot enforce a legal claim.
15. An account which permits payment for purchases to be extended automatically at a given rate of interest if not paid within the normal period.
16. Credit for capital goods; a very large loan which will be repaid over a number of years.
17. A system of billing customers in which the balance owed falls due on a certain day of each month.

Part A—Vocabulary Exercise #3

Directions: Each of the scrambled words below is followed by a definition. Read each definition. Then unscramble the letters to produce a word corresponding to the definition. Write the word in the blank provided.

1. dernered .... given, or paid as due.   1. _____
2. ceirever .... an agent of the court.   2. _____
3. aracchter .. a person's conduct, attitudes, and achievements.   3. _____
4. chinterange .... to alternate.   4. _____
5. tallmentins . debt or sum of money paid at regular intervals.   5. _____

Part B—Study Questions

Directions: Read these questions over before studying the chapter. Then, as you study, you will be looking for the answers. You may want to make a note of the page number where the answer is found alongside the question number. When you have completed the reading, answer the questions on a separate sheet of paper. Explain in your own words whenever possible.
1. What are the two classifications of credit?
2. When does the balance of payments fall due under cycle billing?
3. Who or what is a receiver?
4. What is meant by garnishment of wages?
5. What are the four types of charge accounts?
6. What are the "three C's" for determining credit?
7. Why is credit important to our economy?
8. Why do consumers use credit? Give more than one answer.
9. What is the difference between installment and non-installment credit?
10. How does a charge account differ from a service account?
11. Many retail stores offer revolving charge accounts. How do these accounts work?
12. How does a revolving charge account differ from a budget charge account?
13. Why does selling on credit add extra costs to every sale?
14. Why is it important to have a favorable credit standing?
15. Why is character an important factor in establishing credit?
16. In what cases would a minor and his parent not be held responsible for debts incurred?
17. What is the difference between capital and capacity?
18. Why do many retailers prefer credit customers over cash customers?
19. Why would an individual file for bankruptcy?
20. If you were interested in applying for credit, what steps would you take?
21. Tell and explain your attitude toward charge accounts.

22. Do you feel that the service charges made by retail stores are reasonable? Explain your answer.
23. Explain, in your own words, the importance of keeping purchases and payments in balance.
24. Do you feel that the establishment of legal majority at age 18 is reasonable?
25. Do you feel that the individual consumer, the community, and industry are better off with the use of credit, or not? Explain.

Part C—Organizational Pattern

Directions: In reading this chapter, you will notice that it is organized by means of a series of lists. This exercise is designed to help you recognize the lists that are included and to see how they are related to each other. After reading the chapter, answer the questions below. Use these answers to help you fill in the chart on the next page.

1. What are the different forms of credit? Describe each one.
2. What are the types of charge accounts? Describe each one.
3. What qualifies a person to obtain and use credit?
4. Name and describe ways in which unpaid debts may be handled.

Part D—Enrichment Activities

1. Individual project
   a. Obtain from the instructor, the catalog entitled *Consumer Information*. It lists 200 Federal publications on such subjects as consumer protection, energy, money management, and others.
   b. Look at the section on money management.
   c. Send away for one or more of the booklets on credit (all are free).
   d. Write a summary of the contents of the booklet(s) you receive.
2. Large group or class project
   a. You will need to use the classroom bulletin board, staples and stapler, scissors, construction paper, magazines (if desired), scotch tape, magic markers, etc.
   b. Divide into two smaller groups: for credit and against credit.
   c. The "For" group will determine the advantages of credit; the "Against" group will determine the disadvantages.
   d. Design a bulletin board illustrating advantages vs. disadvantages.
   e. Divide the bulletin board. Each group take half of the area to illustrate the argument.
3. Groups of two or three persons
   a. Obtain from the instructor the booklet entitled, *Making the Most of Your Money*.
   b. Read the part sub-titled "Juan Learns About 'Easy Payment' Plans."
   c. Do one of these two things:
      1. write a reaction report.
      2. plan and perform a skit for the class based on what you read.
4. Individual or group project
   a. Obtain from local department stores information about their credit plans. Obtain also, if the store has one, a copy of the credit application.
   b. Evaluate the information.
   c. Make a comparison of the various credit plans. You may do this in the form of a written report, or on a chart which may be displayed to the class.
   d. Include the following information:
      1. what is the finance charge?
      2. when is the charge assessed?
      3. what is the monthly payment rate?
      4. what steps should a consumer take if there is an error on the bill?
      5. what is your opinion of charges?
5. Individual or small group project
   a. Consult books, pamphlets, and other sources. Interview store managers, bankers, etc. Use other responsible sources of information that you can think of.
   b. Write a report on reasons for credit losses.

152

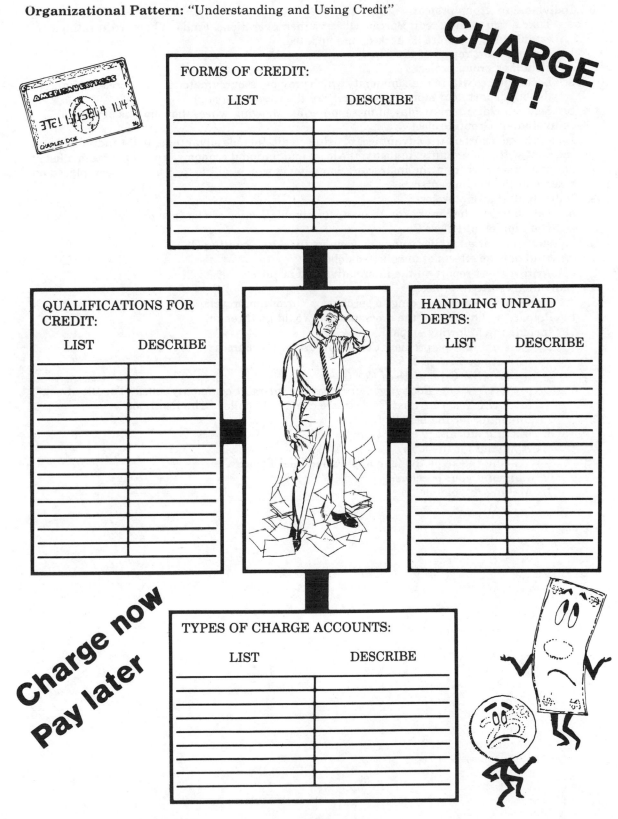

CHARGE IT !

FORMS OF CREDIT:

LIST	DESCRIBE

QUALIFICATIONS FOR CREDIT:

LIST	DESCRIBE

HANDLING UNPAID DEBTS:

LIST	DESCRIBE

Charge now Pay later

TYPES OF CHARGE ACCOUNTS:

LIST	DESCRIBE

153

6. Individual or group project
   a. Take a trip to the Credit Bureau. Observe their operations. Find out how credit ratings are established, monitored, checked, and updated.
   b. Write a short report of the trip.
7. Individual or group project
   a. Locate places within the community which provide resource material about credit. (Hint: Try the big department stores, like Sears. Try the Credit Bureau.)
   b. Set up a classroom display of these materials showing where they may be obtained.
8. Individual or Group Project
   Do a concise report on the advantages of using credit. Include advantages to the individual and the family, the community, industry, the local and national economy. You may obtain a list of possible resources from the instructor. Some items which will help you have been placed on reserve in the media center.
9. Individual or group project
   a. Take a trip to the Finance or Accounts Receivable Section of a large company such as IBM or The Municipal Power Co.,
   b. and/or, visit a smaller company, such as the ABC Printing Co.
   c. Find out the effects of uncollected debts.
   d. Write a short report on the information you acquire.
10. Individual or group project
    a. Make believe you are going to purchase a car or motorcycle.
    b. Prepare a slide-tape of the processes you would go through.
       Include the following steps:
       1. Researching the product. Consult information sources:
          (a) *Consumer's Guide*
          (b) *NADA Official Used Car Guide*
          (c) *Kelley Blue Book New Car Price Manual* (more commonly called "The Blue Book")
          (d) *AIS New Car Cost Guide* (more commonly called "The Red Book")
       2. Shopping for the best buy
       3. Making a deal
       4. Applying for the loan
       5. Tracing the steps the loan application goes through
       6. Enjoying your purchase
       7. Making the payments

KEY TO TEXTBOOKS—Study Guides

Background	Enrichment/Learning Activities
Dilner, 169-190 Estes, 153-176 Herber, 125 Karlin, 127-131 Roe, 53-54 Smith, 160	Burmeister, 108-190 Estes, 177-184; 207-231 Garland, 252-256 Smith, 320-338
Sample Lessons/Exercises/Study Guides	
Dilner, 228-321 Estes, 234-456 Herber, 255-299 Roe, 54-59 Smith, 162-163; 383-391	

See Also:

Piercy, Dorothy. *Reading Activities in Content Areas: An Ideabook for Middle and Secondary Schools.* Boston: Allyn & Bacon, 1976.

ACTIVITY

Using a textbook of your choice, prepare a study guide for one of the chapters. Specific directions for completing this activity include the following:

Planning Phase

1. Do a content analysis.
2. Identify the background or frame of reference which students must possess in order to complete the study guide successfully.
3. List objectives.
4. Describe how you would motivate the reading assignment and how you would help students to establish purposes for the reading.
5. Prepare a structured overview.

Preparation of Student Materials

1. Select the key terms. Prepare vocabulary exercises of various types to teach these terms.
2. Prepare at least 25 questions designed to improve comprehension of the main concept and supporting ideas. Include some questions on each level of comprehension—literal, interpretative, and applied. Ask

some questions which require making inferences, drawing conclusions, evaluation, analysis, and synthesis. (See Appendix A, "Some Elements of the Art of Asking Questions.")

3. Prepare an exercise that stresses the organizational pattern of the chapter. This may be in the form of an outline, chart, or diagram which students are directed to complete.

4. List at least ten enrichment activities. Include some research questions related to the chapter which would require the use of reference materials important in the field.

Do not let these instructions stiffle your imagination. You may do more than this, or do it differently if your subject matter justifies another approach.

For examples which illustrate a variety of study guide formats, see the *Key to Textbooks* on the preceeding page and the *Key to Specific Content Areas* which appears on the inside of the back cover.

Exercise 9:
STUDY GUIDE

Name _____

Title of Textbook _____

Title of Chapter _____

Length of Chapter _____ Approximate Reading Time _____

(Begin your study guide on this page. Add additional pages as needed.)

APPENDIX A

SOME ELEMENTS OF
THE ART OF QUESTIONING

The material in this Appendix has been largely drawn from the chapter entitled, "The Art of Questioning" in *A Handbook for the Teaching of Social Studies,* by the Association of Teachers of Social Studies in the City of New York (Boston: Allyn & Bacon, Inc.) pp. 39-56.

Decide What Questions to Ask:
1. Know the ability of the students. Adjust vocabulary, if necessary, but avoid talking down to students. Do not assume that honor students function at the college level.
2. Formulate a few provocative questions around which a discussion may revolve. Plan these pivotal questions in advance and write them into the lesson plan.
3. Strike a balance between fact questions and thought-provoking questions. Some fact questions may be necessary to aid recall, establish background; but too many may become boring. Thought-provoking questions for which students are unprepared may be frustrating and cause discussion to flounder.
4. Consider the scope of the questions. A broad question may be more suited to the closing of a discussion than to its beginning.

Some Mechanics of Questioning:

1. *Be clear and concise.* Questions must be spoken so that they may be heard. The terms should be understandable and unambiguous. Many times, a context must be established in order to avoid ambiguity; it should be done as concisely as possible. Long, involved introductions easily become confusing.

2. *Ask one question at a time.*

3. *Address questions to the entire class.* Pause. Give the students time to assimilate the question and formulate answers.

4. *Call on a student* to respond *after* the question has been posed. Call on volunteers at first. When the discussion has developed, call on non-volunteers. Avoid causing feelings of harassment, but do expect a response. If the response is inadequate, call on another student; then, later on, direct another question to the person who was unable to respond.

5. *Do not repeat questions.* Call on a student to repeat or rephrase.

6. *Show approval* without imposing judgement. Phrases like, "It would be reasonable to think so", and "That was well expressed" permit the teacher to be approving without dominating.

7. *Ask a variety of questions* to stimulate thinking as well as questions to elicit facts. Ask questions which require students to:

   A. Report Facts
      who, what, where, when, define, describe, identify, list, name, recall, show, tell, write. . .

   B. Demonstrate Understanding
      show why, consider how, what is the cause/effect, compare, contrast, demonstrate, differentiate, distinguish, estimate, explain, extend, illustrate, infer, interpret, predict, relate, rephrase, tell in your own words, explain the meaning of, give an example. . .

   C. Solve Problems
      apply, demonstrate, develop, plan, solve. . .

   D. Analyze (see the parts)
      analyze, categorize, classify, compare, contrast, discriminate, distinguish, recognize. . .

   E. Synthesize (see the whole), Generalize, Hypothesize
      create, develop, formulate, make up, propose, suggest, suppose, assume, infer. . .

   F. Evaluate
      choose, decide, select, evaluate, judge, suppose, what do you consider, what would you do. . .

8. *Use vivid, challenging language.* "Why was Korea called a dagger

160

pointing at the heart of Japan?" has an advantage over "Why did Japan fear Russian expansion in Korea (in the 1900's)?

Some Common Pitfalls in Questioning:

1. *Multiple questions.* Pose a single question. Wait. Add nothing unless it becomes obvious that the question must be rephrased or put in simpler terms.

2. *Yes-No and One Word Answers.* Questions that produce a chorus, promote guessing and fail to sustain a discussion, generally should be avoided. Instead, provide the facts and ask for explanation.

3. *Whiplash questions and Fill-Ins.* Declarative statements that end with a question mark are startling and confusing. "The combination of hydrochloric acid and sodium hydroxide results in what?" would be improved if reworded, "What would be the result of combining HCl and NaOH?"

4. *Leading questions.* Such questions reveal the teacher's bias. The teacher dominates thinking and discussion is frequently shut off. "Don't you *really* think. . .? could be amended, "Do you think. . .? "Why was the Vietnam war necessary?" could be rephrased, "Was the Vietnam war necessary?"

5. *Vague, ambiguous questions.* To ask "What happened in 1600?" promotes guessing. The question is too broad. "What is the difference between books and bicycles?" is too vague. Specify a category, a kind of relationship, a situation calling for an explanation.

6. *Verbose questions.* Questions which become long, highly qualified, and have involved syntax, are confusing. Edit.

7. *Tugging questions.* "Think. What else?" and similar exhortations tug at a pupil's patience and do not stimulate thought.

8. *Questions answered by the teacher.* Such questions probably need to be rethought. Students should be enabled to participate.

Handling Student Responses:

1. *Cross-questioning.* To ensure that a student (especially a very articulate one) understands the implications of an answer, the question might be put, "Why did you say . . .?" Or, "Why did you mention. . .?" Other viewpoints may be solicited from the class.

2. *Avoid repetition of answers.* If an answer is worthy of repetition, it might be rephrased instead by putting it in the form of another question to the class: "Do you agree or disagree that. . .?"

3. *Ensure accuracy.* Correct inaccuracies immediately. In deciding how to deal with them, judge their importance. Minor inaccuracies may be corrected in passing so as not to disturb the flow of thought. However, errors which are likely to result in misunderstanding of a major concept may be subjected to a correction from the class, or to comparison with

161

information from the text and other references. Further questioning may enable students to see the importance of the fact and serve to justify the time spent in correction.

4. *Inadequate answers.* If a student is confused, the teacher may put a question another way by personalizing the situation, "Suppose you were . . ." or may put the problem in reverse, "Suppose it had *not* happened that way . . ."

5. *Unexpected responses.* Unexpected but relevant answers often lead to interesting, worthwhile discussions. If a response is irrelevant, it may help to clarify the topic and re-direct the discussion if students are asked to explain why an issue is not relevant. Digressions are not advisable unless they are significant enough to substitute for the lesson that was planned.

APPENDIX B

EVALUATING TEXTBOOKS AND MATERIALS

Readability is only one aspect to be considered when evaluating a textbook. Consideration must also be given to other factors influencing students' success with reading materials. Accuracy is essential, but quality and manner of presentation are equally important. Even poor readers will be more eager to read material that is eye-catching, appeals to their curiosity and is closely related to their immediate concerns and activities. A colorful book which is well organized and has attractive lay-out throughout with good aids to locate information is less likely to seem a formidable opponent.

Though teachers seldom have a choice of textbooks, they are frequently asked to serve on selection committees and to make suggestions for departmental purchases. Even if these opportunities are not presented, every teacher has an obligation to thoroughly review the basic texts used in his courses in order to use them effectively and to be able to supplement them when necessary.

CHECKLIST FOR EVALUATING TEXTBOOKS*

The general checklist below has been designed by Dr. Richard Lester for use in all subject matter areas and is flexible enough to allow additional criteria to be developed for local conditions and student needs.

---

*Richard L. Lester, "Try Out This Checklist for Evaluating New Textbooks," *Nation's Schools*, 1 (January, 1970), p. 97. Reprinted with the permission of the publisher.

Subject Matter Content. Is the subject matter of the textbook divided in proper proportions according to its significance? Are there any errors in fact or statement? If so, cite page and line, and if possible quote authority to substantiate your charge. Does the book have sufficient scope? Is the material presented in a lively and interesting way? Are students encouraged to learn methods of thinking out solutions and not merely required to memorize details? Is the book written in a clear, concise style? Does the information relate to the environment, general interests and activities of the student? Are questions presented so that they will be understood? Are the reasons for asking the question clear?

Organization. Is there any unifying theme permeating the entire text? Is there an interrelation of chapters, *i. e.* does it have sequence, coherence and articulation? Is there adaptability for varying types of teaching (project method, correspondence study, group study, self study, drill review, *etc.*)?

Authorship. Does the author have professional experience at the particular academic level and in the subject content area? Does the author represent a general philosophy of education compatible with that expressed by the department concerned?

Consideration of Minority Groups. Does the material meet the basic objectives of our democratic society, particularly as it relates to human rights? Is the textbook non-sectarian? Does the author develop the role of American minority groups in a scholarly, factual and effective way? Where appropriate, does the author include a balanced treatment of minority groups in context, rather than through supplementary materials? Is the material likely to create or increase race or class hostility, national rivalries, section prejudice or religious bias? Does the subject matter adequately emphasize the pluralistic nature of our multiracial, multiethnic and multireligious society? Are all groups, especially minorities, represented in their varied and diversified settings? Does the text include the unique contributions of various minority groups?

Copyright Data. Are the materials current with a recent copyright (any material with a copyright date more than five years old should be carefully evaluated)? Do the latest findings in teaching procedures and current technology accompany the recent copyright date? Is a recent copyright date the result of significant change, or a cursory or minor revision of materials from former editions.

Physical Make-up. Is the book attractive? Is the binding substantial in terms of the amount of handling the book may be subjected to? Is the paper of good quality and seemingly durable? Is the printing suitable for the grade level being considered in terms of the students' stage of visual development? Are the words properly spaced and lined to make reading easier? Are photographs, diagrams, maps and graphs, *etc.*, pleasing, colorful, and well located on a page? Are they quality illustrations? Are sufficient illustrations provided? Do the illustrations reflect the pluralistic character of our society?

Aids to Locating Information in the Text. Are the materials arranged in such a manner as to clarify the scope and aims of individual lessons, units and sections? Are the appendices and bibliography adequate in terms of scope and content? How accurate and complete is the index so that specific material may be easily located?

Self-Instructional Aids. Are sufficient illustrations provided the learner in terms of overall course objectives? Are references current? If necessary, do the book and materials have accompanying audiovisual aids, including records, filmstrips, films, tapes and charts? If workbooks are included, are they challenging for the student and do they reinforce major concepts presented in the textbook? Further, are assignments easily corrected? Are exercise materials so organized that the student may easily identify weaknesses in particular areas? Do concise, unit summaries reinforce key learning areas? Are stimulating and interesting activities suggested that will challenge learners to do further independent research? Does the glossary give easily understood definitions of difficult words? Is an attempt made to keep content material current by the issuance of supplementary bulletins?

Adaptability. Does the book suitably fulfill the purpose of the course as you understand it?

Cost. Is the book and/or materials the best available in terms of both educational and financial value?

General Observations.

INDEX

166